an introduction to
tensegrity

UNIVERSITY OF CALIFORNIA PRESS BERKELEY • LOS ANGELES • LONDON

an introduction to
tensegrity

by Anthony Pugh

University of California Press
Berkeley and Los Angeles, California

University of California Press, Ltd.
London, England

Copyright © 1976, by
The Regents of the University of California

ISBN 0-520-02996-8 (clothbound)
ISBN 0-520-03055-9 (paperbound)
Library of Congress Catalog Card Number: 75-5951

Printed in the United States of America

Design: Harlean Richardson
Layout: William H. Snyder

To

Dr. R. Buckminster Fuller

in recognition of his generous inspiration
and encouragement.

CONTENTS

LIST OF PHOTOGRAPHS

1. An expanded octahedron
2. Two-layer systems with six struts (top left), eight struts (top right), and ten struts (bottom)
3. A twelve-strut three-layer diamond-pattern system
4. A cuboctahedron
5. A fifteen-strut three-layer circuit-pattern system
6. A twenty-strut four-layer circuit-pattern system
7. An icosidodecahedron
8. A small rhombicuboctahedron
9. A small rhombicosidodecahedron
10. A four-frequency icosahedron
11. A six-frequency icosahedron (circuit pattern)
12. A two-frequency cube
13. A two-frequency truncated tetrahedron
14. A truncated tetrahedron
15. A snub cube (zigzag pattern)
16. A truncated cube
17. A truncated icosahedron
18. A truncated dodecahedron
19. A great rhombicuboctahedron
20. A great rhombicosidodecahedron
21. A three-frequency dodecahedron
22. A six-frequency octahedron (zigzag pattern)
23. A three-frequency truncated tetrahedron
24. An 84-strut zigzag-pattern figure
25. A 24-strut zigzag-pattern figure
26. A cylindrical zigzag-pattern figure
27. Three joined Tensegrity tetrahedra
28. A framework of expanded octahedra
29. A mast made of six cuboctahedra
30. A dome based on the four-frequency icosahedron
31. A Tensegrity dome with a tensile skin
32. A plywood dome based on the six-frequency icosahedron
33. Close-up of the plywood dome shown in Photograph 32

Preface

Many people have been fascinated by Tensegrity systems, ever since photographs of structures built by R. Buckminster Fuller, Kenneth Snelson and others began to appear in books and magazines. The way that the struts of the figures do not touch one another, but appear to hang within the tendons as if by magic, excites the interest of people who would not pay much attention to more orthodox structures. Unfortunately, apart from a few of the writings of R. Buckminster Fuller, who coined the word Tensegrity, little reliable information has been published on the subject.

This volume explains the concept of Tensegrity and describes a large range of figures. Since Tensegrity systems are so different from other structures, the best way to learn about them is through building and studying models, especially since erroneous ideas can be developed if one attempts to understand Tensegrity from photographs or from models built by someone else. Instructions for building models of all the figures described in the book appear in the appendices.

People from many backgrounds, especially artists, architects, designers, and engineers, will find a study of Tensegrity a very valuable experience. The symmetries of the figures and the problems of assembly make the business of building models a challenging and stimulating exercise in three dimensions. In creating stable arrangements by balancing tensile and compressive forces, one develops a feeling for the roles these forces play in stable structures.

Tensegrity is still in the early stages of its development, and it is difficult to predict its most important uses. Though this book suggests a few structural applications, there is a good chance that the most important applications will lie in fields other than structure.

The author gratefully thanks the following for their help and encouragement: Dr. R. Buckminster Fuller; Mike Jerome; Professor A. Douglas Jones; Michael Burton; The Science Research Council of the United Kingdom; Hugh Kenner; Bill Perk and the faculty and students of the Department of Design, Southern Illinois University at Carbondale.

1. Background, Definitions, and General Characteristics

Everything from a speck of dust to the universe has forces acting on it or stresses acting within it which are trying to deform it or cause it to move. Even in outer space, where there would appear to be no external gravitational pull, an object will have internal stresses from mass attraction between its parts.

A building likewise has many forces acting on it: those caused by its own weight, the weight of its occupants, and the weight of its furnishings, machinery, and stores. It may also be subjected to such external forces as snow on its roof, wind pressures, earth tremors, vibrations, and impacts from automobiles, aeroplanes, and uprooted trees. These forces pass through the structure, pushing on some components, pulling on others. The force which pushes on a component, trying to shorten it, is called a compressive force, while the force which pulls on a component, trying to extend it, is called a tensile force.

Until the middle of the nineteenth century most of the materials available to the building industry were effective in resisting compressive forces, but few were capable of withstanding even moderate tensile stress. Wood was one of the few materials which could withstand tension, but its tensile strength hardly rivaled the compressive strengths and durability of stone and brick. As a consequence, buildings were designed so that large tensile stresses were not developed in them. Though this might appear to prohibit the design of exciting structures, the great medieval cathedrals should not be forgotten. The few man-made structures of the past in which relatively large tensile forces were allowed to develop, such as the delicate suspension bridges constructed from ropes and creepers by the people of so-called primitive societies, could not carry heavy loads and required frequent repair and replacement.

During the past one hundred years, durable materials with very high tensile strengths have been developed; however, few buildings have been designed to exploit them. R. Buckminster Fuller noticed the contrast between this lack of engineering imagination and the more sophisticated techniques of nature. (Perhaps this contrast should not surprise us; man has only been building structures for a few thousand years, whereas nature has been experimenting for millions.) Fuller noticed that nature always used a balance of tension and compression, and that the compressive components were usually much heavier and bulkier than the tensile components. This is necessary because a tensile component need only be thick enough to take the imposed load, whereas a compressive component needs an additional thickness of material to prevent it from buckling. For example, a long wire will support a considerable load in tension, but it will not take a very large load in compression. A common way of preventing the wire from buckling when it is compressed is to use a thicker piece of wire, and the longer the wire, the thicker it must be. Similarly, in the human body the heavy bones are necessary to carry the compressive forces, while the lighter tendons are sufficient to carry the tensile forces. Another vivid example of the efficiency of tensile elements can be found in a drop of water or quicksilver, where the attractions among the molecules create an invisible tensile "skin" to hold the drop together.

Buckminster Fuller was also aware of many man-made structures with higher performances than those used in the building industry. The seemingly fragile arrangements of masts and fixed rigging on a sailing ship, for example, take punishing loads to enable the wind to move the colossal weight of the ship through the water. The designers of those ships had a great feeling for tensile forces, allowing large loads to be transmitted around the hulls. The captains and sailors of such ships seem to have understood the role of tension in a structure, as there are records of them binding weakened hulls with chains and ropes to reach a friendly port. Most contemporary architects and builders would have used internal strutting to combat such structural weaknesses, making the situation worse in many cases. The aeroplane is another human creation whose structure is carefully engineered. Since weight was so crucial, the early aircraft were made as light as possible, and we must admire those who trusted their lives to structures with such delicate wooden struts and thin tie-rods. Weight is just as critical today, and many ingenious methods are used to minimize the weight of modern aircraft.

During the 1920s many architects looked at ships and aircraft in the search for a new aesthetic, but Buckminster Fuller was interested in how their performances could be transferred to the archaic building industry he saw around him. Aware that man had neglected the role of tension in the design of structures, and that there should be a balance of tensile and compressive forces, Fuller was ready to develop the idea of Tensegrity when Kenneth Snelson showed him some early Tensegrity models in 1948.

Definitions and General Characteristics

In any structural system, there must be some kind of continuity to allow forces to be transmitted from one part of the structure to another. In most man-made structures, this continuity is achieved through the compression members, with the occasional tension member being incorporated where it cannot be avoided. In a Tensegrity system the continuity is achieved through a continuous network of tensile elements, the compression elements being discontinuous. This was why Buckminster Fuller coined the word *Tensegrity*, a contraction of *tensional integrity*. Thus, a Tensegrity system can be defined as follows:

A Tensegrity system is established when a set of discontinuous compressive components interacts with a set of continuous tensile components to define a stable volume in space.

It will be noticed that such words as *structure*, *strut*, and *tendon* are not used in this definition. The word *structure* is not used, since there is a chance that the most important applications of Tensegrity may not be in the field of structures. The words *strut* and *tendon* are not used here (although they are used, for convenience, in other parts of the book), as the components are not always *struts* and *tendons*. For example, the figure shown in Photograph 4 has compressive elements which are triangles of struts, and the figure shown in Photograph 31 has a tensile skin, instead of a network of tendons. An important point about the definition is that it states that the tensile components are continuous and the compressive components, discontinuous. If the compressive components were continuous, the tensile network would not always need to be continuous, thereby losing the tensional integrity of the system.

If a few structures, especially the simpler figures described in Chapter 2, it will be found that struts touch one another at points other than their ends. This is because they are trying to pass through the same point and are displacing one another. In such cases it may be worth connecting them to a central node, as is shown in Chapter 2. Since such figures do not have truly discontinuous compression units, there is a temptation to dismiss them as not being true Tensegrity systems; but one should not be too ready to ignore any system in one's early experiments, as later discoveries may prove it to be an important link in a series of figures.

Though these structures may at first appear to be so different from other types of structure, Buckminster Fuller has shown how similar they are to bubbles, balloons, and airsupported structures. In a balloon the enclosed air is at a higher pressure than the surrounding air and pushes outwards against the inwards-pulling skin. In a model of a Tensegrity system, the struts push outwards like the air inside a balloon, and the tendons pull inwards like the skin of a balloon. In both types of systems, the tension-carrying elements are already under tension, and the compression-carrying elements are already under compression. If the air pressure inside a balloon is increased, the tension forces in the skin will become greater, but that balloon will now be harder to deform. A similar situation occurs with a Tensegrity system, and it will be found that increasing the forces in the components will increase the strength and load-bearing capacity of the system.

A balloon is very sensitive to vibrations and passes them almost instantaneously around the figure. Vibrations pass round many Tensegrity systems in a similar way, as can be seen if one of the tendons of a model is plucked. In situations where vibrations are unacceptable, they can usually be prevented by adding extra tendons, as is shown in later chapters.

A model of a Tensegrity system can be deformed by pressing down on it, but it will spring back to its original shape once that force is removed. The same thing happens if one is to press down on a balloon. One can press down too hard on a model of a Tensegrity system and cause it to break, but one can also push too hard on a balloon and rupture that, too.

The preceding paragraphs have made a few general observations on Tensegrity systems, and others will be mentioned in subsequent chapters. Once the reader has constructed a few models, he may be able to make other observations more appropriate to his own background and interests.

2. Some Simple Figures

Though it may be tempting to start by building models of some
of the more complex figures described later, this will usually
result in frustrating failure, simply because the necessary skills
have yet to be developed. The best way of developing those skills
is by building some simple figures, using the materials and
techniques described in Appendix 1. During this time the reader
will learn how to manipulate the struts and tendons and how to
watch for, and deal with, rubber bands which are slipping off
the struts. The reader will also learn how the struts and tendons
act on one another and should be able to develop some valuable
insights into Tensegrity.

Some readers may think it is not worth spending time on the
simple figures, but some of them are very significant and are
related to the larger, more complex ones. At this stage, no
figure should be excluded from consideration on the grounds
that it is not a proper Tensegrity figure for any reason, as it may
turn out to be related to other, more conventional Tensegrity
figures. The reader may be surprised by the number and variety
of figures that can be built, as illustrated by the selection of
figures described in this chapter. Most of these figures can be
built by holding the struts in one's hands, by taping them
together, by wedging them in plasticine, or by using some other
simple technique for holding them while the rubber bands are
added.

Two-dimensional Figures

The simplest figures (Diagram 2.1) are essentially two-dimensional,
though they do not lie completely flat, because of the thickness of
their struts. The simplest of these, Figure 1, consists of two struts

2.1

Figure 1

which define the long diagonals of a square and four tendons which define its edges. Figure 2 shows a larger polygon — a hexagon — whose long diagonals are defined by three struts and whose edges are defined by six tendons. This idea can be extended to create an octagon (Figure 3) and even larger polygons.

One of the problems with the figures in Diagram 2.1 is that many struts pass through the centres of the polygons, so their combined thicknesses distort the polygons. There are other polygons, however, which have open space at their centres, as in Figures 4 through 7 (Diagram 2.2). In these figures, each strut end is joined to another to create circuits of struts within outer tendon circuits. Larger versions of this type of figure can be produced.

Figures 8 and 9 (Diagram 2.3) belong to another family of polygonal forms where open space is developed at the centre. In these figures the strut ends do not touch one another. Larger versions of this type of figure can also be built.

Figures with Struts Passing Through Their Centres

Having established a range of two-dimensional figures, the next step is to see what can be built in three dimensions. A central "mast" can be added to Figure 1 so that half the strut protrudes above the square and half below it (Diagram 2.4). Both ends of this strut can be guyed to the four corners of the original square with rubber-band tendons. The twelve tendons of the resulting figure (Figure 10), define the twelve edges of an *octahedron*, after which polyhedron this figure is named.

The octahedron has three struts, each of which spans between two vertices, as shown in Diagram 2.4. Each strut passes the other two struts at right angles at the centre of the figure. Since all three struts cannot pass through the centre simultaneously, the figure will be slightly irregular unless a special junction is made at the centre for six half-struts to meet there, as shown in Diagram 2.5.

A model of this figure is easily made by grasping the three struts in one hand and adding the rubber bands with the other. Once complete, the figure can be manipulated and distorted to explore

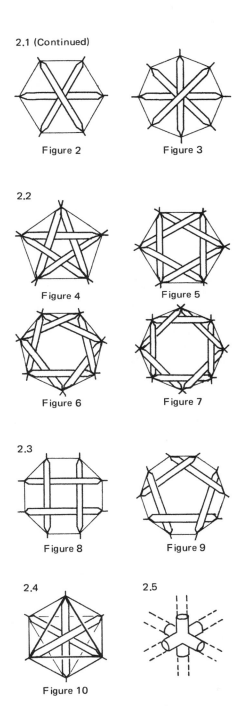

2.1 (Continued)

Figure 2   Figure 3

2.2

Figure 4   Figure 5

Figure 6   Figure 7

2.3

Figure 8   Figure 9

2.4   2.5

Figure 10

the wide range of variations that can be made in its overall shape. Although this figure is very simple, it is very significant and will be mentioned frequently in this volume.

Since the octahedron is one of the five Platonic polyhedra, it is worth looking at the other Platonic polyhedra to see whether Tensegrity figures can be based on any of them. In the octahedron the struts spanned between opposite vertices, which is obviously impossible with a tetrahedron. However, a *Tetrahedron* (Figure 11) can be formed from four struts, each of which spans from its centre to one of its vertices, together with six tendons which define its edges, as shown in Diagram 2.6. This figure will collapse if it is built with rubber-band tendons, so it must be built from less elastic tendons, such as fishing line.

A *cube* (Figure 12) can be created from four struts and twelve tendons. The struts span between opposite pairs of vertices, and the tendons define the edges of the figure, as shown in Diagram 2.7. This figure, like the octahedron, can be made by holding the struts in one hand and adding the rubber bands with the other. From this model it can be appreciated that a variety of prismatic shapes can be made by adjusting the lengths of the tendons.

If six more rubber-band tendons are added diagonally across the faces of a cube to define a tetrahedron, as shown in Diagram 2.8a, the figure will change shape, to produce Figure 13 (Diagram 2.8). One end of each strut will be forced outwards, and the tendons will then define the edges of a tetrahedron with a tetrahedron added to each face. The four strut ends which project the farthest define the vertices of a large tetrahedron.

An *icosahedron* (Figure 14) can be formed with six struts, each of which spans between opposite pairs of vertices, and thirty tendons, each of which defines an edge of the icosahedron. Similarly, a *dodecahedron* (Figure 15) can be formed from ten struts and thirty tendons. In both of these figures (Diagram 2.9), however, there is great congestion because so many struts are trying to pass through the centres of the figures.

Returning to the idea of adding masts to the two-dimensional figures described earlier, many other possibilities can be tried. Figure 16 for example, was made by adding two of the two-strut

2.6

Figure 11

2.7

Figure 12

2.8

 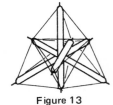

a   Figure 13

2.9

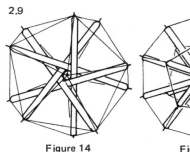

Figure 14   Figure 15

squares (Figure 1) to a long central mast and stabilizing them with extra tendons (Diagram 2.10). Many variations can be made on this theme, to produce further figures.

Triangles of Struts

Figure 17 (Diagram 2.11) can be produced by adding a central mast to the hexagonal figure with three struts (Figure 2). In this figure the tendons define the edges of a hexagonal dipyramid. As is true of many other simple figures, the centre of this figure is cluttered with struts, but the three struts of the original hexagon can be rearranged to form a triangle, as shown in Figure 18. In that figure the triangle is suspended from the mast, creating plenty of space at the middle. Figure 18 introduces the use of triangles of struts, an idea that can be developed further.

Figure 19 (Diagram 2.12) shows a figure where two struts have been added to the central mast to form a second triangle of struts. Two more tendons will be needed to stabilize the figure, which will then have six struts and eight tendons. If two more struts are added to the central mast, together with two more tendons, a third triangle of struts can be formed, to produce Figure 20 (Diagram 2.12). A further 2 struts joined to the central mast, stabilized with 2 more tendons, produce Figure 21. Many other things can be done with triangles or other polygons of struts.

Single-layer Figures

An interesting figure can be created by removing 3 tendons from a rubber-band model of the octahedron (Figure 10). The three tendons to be removed are those that pass in front of struts, indicated by arrows in Diagram 2.13a. Those tendons can be found by turning the model until a complete strut can be seen unobstructed by other struts. The band to remove is the one in front of the strut, as indicated in Diagram 2.13b. When removing the bands, hold the struts firmly in case the wrong band is removed and the structure collapses. If this is done correctly, the struts can be released to produce Figure 22.

Figure 22 has nine tendons and three struts, three tendons meeting at each strut end, and it is interesting to find that the

2.10

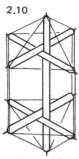

Figure 16

2.11

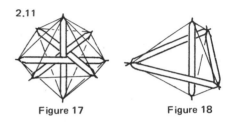

Figure 17   Figure 18

2.12

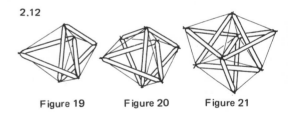

Figure 19   Figure 20   Figure 21

2.13

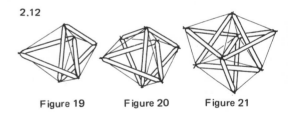

a   b   Figure 22

struts do not touch one another. The figure is symmetrical about
an axis which passes through the centres of two triangles of
tendons, which could be regarded as the top and bottom of the
figure. If the figure is viewed from one of its "ends", it can be
seen that the one end triangle is twisted in relationship to the
other. Because of the twist the "sides" of the figure consist of
three equally distorted diamonds of tendons, each having a strut
defining its longer diagonal, as shown in Diagram 2.14.

2.14

If three of the tendons on this figure were disconnected, three
additional tendons and a strut could be added, to produce
Figure 23, with four struts and twelve tendons (Diagram 2.15).
The two ends of this figure would be squares, and if viewed from
the end, the one square will be twisted in relationship to the
other. This figure can be made from scratch by holding four
struts in one hand and adding rubber bands with the other hand.
Anyone finding this difficult could wedge the struts into plasticine
to hold them while adding the rubber bands.

2.15

Figure 23

Similarly, three of the tendons on Figure 23 can be disconnected, to allow the addition of three more tendons and one
more strut, to produce Figure 24 (Diagram 2.16). That figure has
pentagonal ends. The easiest way of making it is to construct the
four-strut figure and then connect the fifth strut before removing
redundant tendons. Further figures can be made by adding more
struts and tendons, as suggested by the six-strut figure with
hexagonal ends (Figure 25).

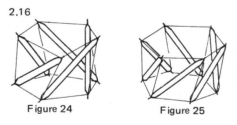

2.16

Figure 24   Figure 25

Clearly, Figures 22-25 are related to one another. It will be
noticed that the ones with many struts need shorter tendons at
the top and bottom than at the sides; in fact, some figures may
collapse if the top and bottom tendons are too long. From the
description of how these figures were evolved, it can be
appreciated that if three tendons were disconnected and the
figure opened out, the arrangement of struts and tendons shown
in Diagram 2.17 would result. (In practice it may be difficult to
actually open out a model like that, but it is hoped that the
general idea is apparent.) From such an arrangement it can be
seen that the struts form a single layer, so these figures are called
single-layer figures.

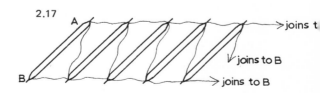

2.17

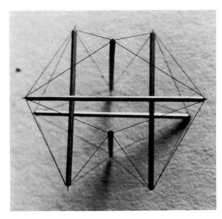

1. An expanded octahedron

The Expanded Octahedron (Icosahedron)

Perhaps the best known, and certainly one of the most impressive Tensegrity figures has six struts which do not touch one another and twenty-four tendons. Figure 26 (see Diagram 2.18 and Photograph 1) is popularly called an icosahedron, but it is really an expanded version of the octahedron (Figure 10) and will be referred to as the expanded octahedron in this volume. (The reasons for the name are explained at the end of Chapter 4.) Since most readers will want to build this model, several methods of constructing it are given, so the reader can choose whichever suits him best.

It is worth learning as much as possible about any figure before trying to build it, and this one is no exception. The expanded octahedron has six struts which are arranged in three pairs, each pair defining a plane which cuts the planes defined by the other pairs of struts at right angles. The struts can be arranged across the six faces of a cube with each strut bisecting one of its faces, as shown in Diagram 2.19a. The figure has twenty-four tendons, which form diamond shapes about each strut, the diamonds being creased along their longer axes, as shown in Diagram 2.19b. The tendons also define eight triangles between the diamond shapes. If six tendons were added between

2.18

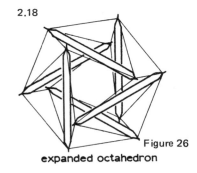

Figure 26

expanded octahedron

2.19

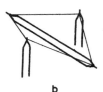

a   b

the ends of parallel struts, as indicated by the dotted lines in Diagram 2.19c, the thirty tendons would define the thirty edges of an icosahedron; hence the original name of this figure. But it will be found that those added tendons have to be much shorter than the original twenty-four and that they will cause the figure to contract. This is one reason for calling the figure an expanded octahedron rather than an icosahedron.

2.19 (continued)

c

One method of building a model is to tape or tie the six struts securely to a small cube made from card, wood, or plasticine in the arrangement shown in Diagram 2.19a. The twenty-four rubber-band tendons can then be added, to define a diamond about each strut. Once all the tendons have been added (it is worth counting them as they are added) and all six diamonds have been defined, the central cube can be released and removed. With practice, it is possible to dispense with the box and hold all the struts in one hand, adding the tendons with the other. However, the beginner may find the latter method very frustrating, and tiring on the fingers because of the time he may have to spend wondering where to add the next rubber band.

Instead of the struts being fixed to a central cube, they can be lashed together with string or rubber bands. In this method each pair of struts must be outside one of the other pairs of struts but inside the third pair. In Diagram 2.20 the pair of struts marked *A* is outside the pair marked *B* but inside the pair marked *C*. The pair of struts marked *B* is outside the pair marked *C* but inside the pair marked *A*. The pair marked *C* is outside the pair marked *A* but inside the pair marked *B*. Once the struts have been lashed together correctly, the twentyfour tendons can be added as before. Once the tendons have been added correctly, the central lashing can be undone, and the struts will spring into position.

2.20

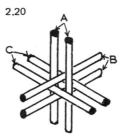

Once the model with rubber-band tendons has been completed, smarter struts and less elastic tendons can be substituted, as described in Appendix 1. The tendons for a model with struts 9 inches long will be approximately 5 1/2 inches long. If fishing line is being used and a tightly tensed model is wanted, the tendons should be slightly shorter (approximately 5 5/16 inches long); they will all stretch to the correct length when the final tendon is added. Once the model is finished, any tendons which are too long can be shortened by putting half hitches over one of the nails, and any which are too short can be replaced with ones of the correct length. Though it might seem that it would be quicker to tie the tendons in the first place, it is actually much quicker to build the rubber-band model first.

Once the model is completed, a parallel pair of struts can be grasped and forced towards each other, and the other struts will move towards one another at a similar rate and the figure will contract evenly. Alternatively, if the struts are pulled apart, the other struts move apart at a similar rate, and the figure expands evenly. Forcing the struts together is equivalent to decreasing the amount of air in a balloon, causing the figure to contract evenly; pulling the struts apart is equivalent to increasing the amount of air inside a balloon, causing it to expand. It should be noted that, though the forcing together of struts works well with models with tendons which are not too elastic, such as fishing line, it will not work with models with very elastic tendons, such as rubber bands, since they deform too easily.

Variations on the Expanded Octahedron

As with other Tensegrity figures, the expanded octahedron can be manipulated and altered to create other figures. If a model of an expanded octahedron is made from rubber bands, one pair of parallel struts can be forced together and replaced by a single strut to produce Figure 27. This figure has five struts and twenty tendons. In Diagram 2.21, the strut which replaces the pair which were forced together appears solid.

Two pairs of struts can be forced together and replaced by single struts to produce Figure 28 which has four struts and sixteen tendons. The two struts which replace the two pairs of struts appear solid in Diagram 2.22. If the third pair of struts were forced together, a figure with three struts and twelve tendons would be produced, the *octahedron* (Figure 10).

2.21

Figure 27

2.22

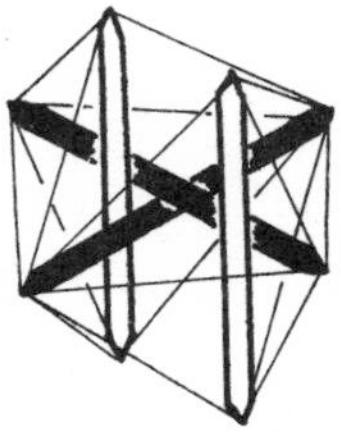

Figure 28

Other figures can be derived from the expanded octahedron, one of the most important of which is described at the beginning of Chapter 6.

Conclusion

There is a very large number of these simple forms, only a few of which have been described here. Some people may be tempted to ignore these simple figures, but they are important and much can be learned from them. Many of them have different characteristics from the more conventional Tensegrity figures and provoke stimulating thoughts into the basic definition of Tensegrity, which could result in the evolution of an entirely different type of figure. In fact, these simple figures are worth returning to after studying the more complex figures described later.

Most readers will build their models with rubber bands as tendons. If they wish to keep some of them for future reference, it would be worth replacing the rubber bands with fishing-line tendons, as described in Appendix 1. The lengths of the tendons can be worked out by measuring the lengths of the rubber bands, taking averages when appropriate, and making allowances for the elasticity of the fishing line. One benefit of tying up one or two of these models with the fishing line is that it is good practice for tying up the larger models described in later chapters.

3. The Diamond Pattern

Single-layer Figures

A series of single-layer figures, such as the five-strut figure shown in Diagram 3.1a, were described in Chapter 1. The tendons of each figure defined similar polygons at each "end" and diamond shapes on the "sides." Each diamond was creased along its longer diagonal, which was occupied by one of the struts, as shown in Diagram 3.1b.

Figures whose tendons are arranged in diamond shapes with struts defining the longer diagonals of those diamonds are called *diamond-pattern systems.*

Two-layer Figures

The expanded octahedron (Figure 26, Diagram 3.2) is another figure in which sets of tendons define diamond shapes which are creased along their longer diagonals, which are defined by the struts.

If an expanded octahedron is placed on one of its triangles of tendons, three of the struts will touch the ground and three will be suspended in midair. In other words, the struts are in two distinct layers, and the figure can be regarded as a six-strut two-layer system. If one of the triangles of tendons were considered the top of the figure and the opposite triangle the bottom, six of the tendons could be disconnected, allowing the figure to be opened out approximately as in Diagram 3.3. This is only a diagrammatic representation of the arrangement, as in practice the struts would overlap one another, but the two layers of struts can be seen very clearly.

Diagram 3.3 can be extended, by adding extra struts and tendons, to represent a series of two-layer figures. Diagram 3.4

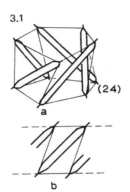

3.1

(24)

a

b

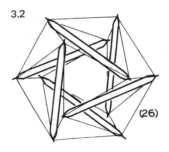

3.2

(26)

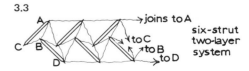

3.3

A

C B

D

→joins to A

↘to C

↖ ↗to B

↘to D

six-strut two-layer system

2. Two-layer systems with six struts (top left), eight struts (top right), and ten struts (bottom)

represents a two-layer figure with eight struts and thirty-two tendons. The top and bottom polygons of tendons are squares, as may be deduced from the diagram or seen in Photograph 2. Though the expanded octahedron was symmetrical about several axes, this figure is only symmetrical about an axis passing through the centres of its two square, end polygons.

If two more struts and eight more tendons are added to the figure in Diagram 3.4, as shown in Diagram 3.5, a figure with ten struts and forty tendons will be represented. There will be five struts in each layer, and the ends defined by the tendons will be pentagonal. It can be seen in Photograph 2 that this figure, like the previous one, is only symmetrical about one axis, the axis passing through the centres of its two pentagonal ends.

Further struts and tendons can be added to the basic diagram, as shown for a twelve-strut, two-layer system in Diagram 3.6. However, these larger figures are not as stable as the smaller ones, and in some cases the tendons at top and bottom have to be made shorter to prevent a model from sagging. From Photograph 2 it can be seen that these two-layer figures are approximately cylindrical and of varying diameters, depending on the numbers of struts in each layer.

3. A twelve-strut three-layer
diamond-pattern system

Three-layer Figures

Three-layer diamond-pattern systems can be built, as represented
by the set shown in Diagram 3.7. The diagrams in this set are
similar to those of the two-layer systems and are created by
disconnecting a few tendons, to allow the figures to be laid out
flat. In practice some of the struts would have to overlap to allow
a figure to lie flat, but the diagrams do show the basic relationships between struts and tendons. Each of these figures is
approximately cylindrical, tapering at top and bottom like a
wooden barrel. The more struts there are in each layer, the larger
the diameters of these cylinders are, with the ends of the
nine-strut figure being triangles, those of the twelve-strut figure
squares, and so on. Three-layer figures with more than six struts
in each layer are possible but tend to be less stable than the
smaller ones. Photograph 3 shows the twelve-strut three-layer
figure.

Larger Figures

The diagrams for the three-layer figures can be extended to
represent four-layer figures, as shown by Diagram 3.8, for a
twenty-strut four-layer system. As with examples shown earlier,
four-layer systems are not very stable if they have more than six

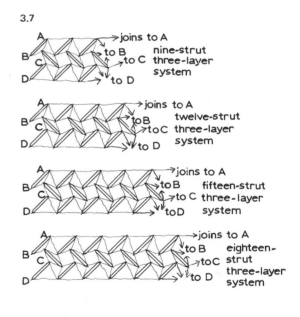

struts in each layer. These figures are approximately cylindrical, their diameters depending on the number of struts in each layer. The tendons in the top and bottom circuits need to be shortened to reduce the diameters of the tops and bottoms of the figures, resulting in barrel-shaped cylinders. This curvature of the sides strengthens the figures. It is possible to build figures with more than four layers of struts, but such figures are not very strong if there are more than three or four struts in each layer. It should be remembered that extra tendons can sometimes be added to strengthen an apparently flimsy figure.

Constructing Models

There are many ways of building models of these figures, but the method suggested in Appendix 2 is the quickest and easiest one for a beginner. Any of the figures described in this chapter could be built by this method, but it might be best to build the twelve-strut three-layer figure (Photograph 3) used as an example, since it will be referred to in Chapter 4.

4. The Circuit Pattern

The Circuit Pattern

The tendons of the twelve-strut three-layer figure described in
Chapter 3 define eight triangles and six squares, as well as the
basic diamonds of the figure. If an opposite pair of the squares
are forced towards one another, the whole system twists and
contracts. The creases down the longer axes of each diamond also
become sharper, and the struts at opposite ends of the system's
shorter axis move closer to one another. If these strut ends are
forced together and joined, the tendons double up and a new
strut-tendon relationship is established, as shown in Diagram 4.1b.

Characteristics of the Pattern

When the strut ends of the twelve-strut three-layer figure are
joined (see Photograph 4), four triangles of struts are formed.
Each triangle interweaves with the other triangles, passing inside
one, outside the next, inside the next, and so on. This characteristic prompted R. Buckminster Fuller to call this type of figure a
Basketry Tensegrity. Joining the strut ends causes the tendons
to double up; each pair can then be replaced by a single tendon,
to reduce the number of components. Though the junctions of
struts and tendons are slightly more complex, there are only
half as many as there were before the ends were joined. The
new figure is smaller than it was before the struts were joined, but
it is a lot sturdier.

It could be claimed that this figure is not a true Tensegrity
structure, since the concept of discontinuous compression has
been violated by joining the strut ends. However, it is now the
triangles which are the compression units, not the individual

4.1

strut ends move
towards one another

fold becomes sharper

a

strut ends joined.
tendons double up.

b

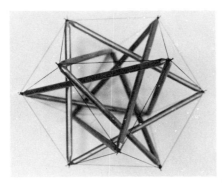

4. A cuboctahedron

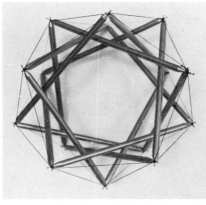

5. A fifteen-strut three-layer circuit-
pattern system

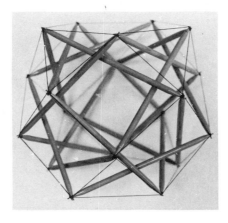

6. A twenty-strut four-layer circuit-
pattern system

struts, and since the triangles do not touch one another as they interweave, these figures can still be regarded as true Tensegrity structures.

A final point to note is that the tendons of this figure define the edges of a cuboctahedron, one of the Archimedean polyhedra.

The strut ends of many other diamond-pattern figures can be joined to produce figures similar to the one just discussed, as can be seen in Photograph 5, which shows the figure evolved from the fifteen-strut three-layer system, and in Photograph 6, which shows the figure derived from the twenty-strut four-layer system. If several of these figures are compared, the following common characteristics can be established:

1. The tendons define the edges of a polyhedron, which need be neither regular nor semiregular. Four tendons and two struts meet at each junction to form a vertex of the figure, so at least four edges must meet at each vertex of a polyhedron used as a basis for a circuit-pattern figure.

2. When the struts are joined, they form circuits of struts, hence the name *circuit pattern* for this strut-tendon relationship. The circuits of struts follow the lines of circuits of tendons, which can be traced on models of appropriate polyhedra.

3. The circuits of struts interweave with each other, passing under one circuit, then over the next, under the next, and so on.

4. A network of tendons surrounds a series of circuits of struts, the tendons pulling inwards like the skin of a balloon, the struts pushing outwards like the air in the balloon.

5. There is a junction of struts and tendons outside the midpoint of each strut, so there will be the same number of junctions as there are struts.

Being aware of these common characteristics can be a great help when working on figures using this strut-tendon relationship, both for finding new figures and for spotting mistakes when building models. But, though these characteristics can be very useful in establishing new figures, one should always be prepared to look beyond them if they would exclude an otherwise valid Tensegrity figure.

Figures Based on the Platonic and Archimedean Polyhedra

Since circuit-pattern figures are usually based on polyhedra which have four edges meeting at each vertex, the octahedron is the only Platonic polyhedron (Diagram 4.2) which can form the basis of such a system. At first this polyhedron would appear to be too small for circuits of struts to interweave within it; however, the octahedron in Figure 10 could be regarded as a circuit-pattern figure, with three circuits which are pairs of struts which merge to form its three single struts.

There are four Archimedean polyhedra — the cuboctahedron, the icosidodecahedron, the small rhombicuboctahedron, and the small rhombicosidodecahedron — which have four edges meeting at each vertex and which can be used as bases for circuit-pattern systems.

The *cuboctahedron* (Photograph 4) has twelve struts of equal length, which form four equilateral triangles which interweave without touching one another. The twenty-four tendons are equal in length and define the edges of a cuboctahedron (Diagram 4.3).

The *icosidodecahedron* (Photograph 7) has thirty struts of equal length, which form six pentagonal circuits which interweave without touching one another. The sixty tendons are equal in length and define the edges of an icosidodecahedron (Diagram 4.4).

The figure in Photograph 8 has twenty-four struts and forty-eight tendons and was originally visualized as a *small rhombicuboctahedron* (Diagram 4.5a), as it was thought that its tendons would define the edges of that polyhedron. The struts were to form six square circuits, arranged in three pairs, each pair being parallel to a plane which would intersect the other squares at right angles. But, when the first model was built, twelve of the square faces of the small rhombicuboctahedron twisted to form bent rhombic shapes, as shown in Diagram 4.5b, so that the tendons defined all but twelve of the edges of a *snub cube*. The figure had behaved like a balloon, and the tendons, like the skin of a balloon, had forced it into as small a volume

4.2

tetrahedron   octahedron   icosahedron

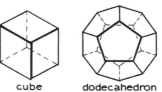

cube   dodecahedron

4.3

cuboctahedron

4.4

icosidodecahedron

4.5

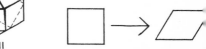

small
rhombicuboctahedron   distortion of a square fa
a   b

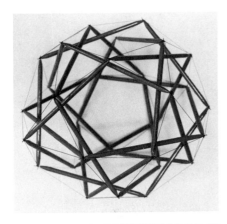

7. An icosidodecahedron

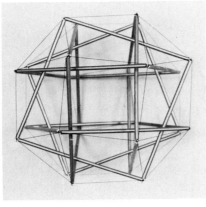

8. A small rhombicuboctahedron

as possible, the snub cube having a smaller volume than the small rhombicuboctahedron. The six square circuits of struts arranged themselves in three pairs as predicted, each pair being parallel to a plane which intersected the other squares at right angles. Twelve extra tendons might be added to the figure, to define the rest of the edges of the snub cube, but these are not necessary to ensure stability. If the original forty-eight tendons are to define the edges of an undistorted small rhombicuboctahedron, an extra tendon must be added to each of the twelve appropriate square faces to prevent them from distorting.

The figure in Photograph 9 has sixty struts and 120 tendons and is the largest circuit-pattern system derived directly from an

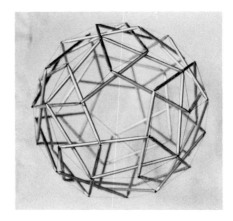

9. A small rhombicosidodecahedron

Archimedean polyhedron. This figure was originally visualized as
a *small rhombicosidodecahedron* (Diagram 4.6), but, as with the
previous figure, the tendons force the figure to contract so that its
square faces become bent rhomboids and the tendons define all
but thirty of the edges of a *snub dodecahedron*. Extra tendons
could be added to define those thirty edges, but they are not
necessary to ensure stability. As with the figures described
previously, an extra tendon must be added to each square face
if an undistorted small rhombicosidodecahedron is needed.
The sixty struts of this figure form twelve pentagonal circuits
which interweave without touching one another.

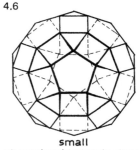

4.6

small
rhombicosidodecahedron

Construction of Models

Instructions for assembling models of all the figures described in
this chapter can be found in Appendix 3. Though a cuboctahedron
could be built by joining the ends of a twelve-strut three-layer
diamond-pattern system, the method given in Appendix 3 is
quicker. An advantage of building it that way is that it will
familiarize the reader with the general method for building all
circuit-pattern figures. Some readers may be tempted to try to
build a cuboctahedron by constructing a triangle of struts and then
adding the other three triangles to it. Though this might appear to
be a good, quick way of building a model, it is *very* difficult to do
correctly, as the triangles interweave in a three-dimensional

manner which most people find difficult to visualize. The small rhombicosidodecahedron takes a long time to build, as it has so many components, but it behaves just like the smaller ones.

Circuit-Pattern Systems Derived from Other Diamond-Pattern Systems

Circuit-pattern systems can be created from most diamond-pattern systems, including the multilayer systems described in Chapter 3. Though those diamond-pattern systems were not very strong if they had more than four layers of struts or more than six struts in each layer, circuit-pattern systems which exceed those limits are often very stable. This is partly because joining the strut ends stiffens the figure and partly because the struts and tendons of the circuit-pattern figures meet at more favourable angles. Though joining the strut ends results in a figure which is stronger, it should be remembered that it will be smaller.

Since a name like *fifteen-strut three-layer system* could refer to either a diamond-pattern figure or a circuit-pattern figure, it is a good idea to add the name of the pattern — for example, *fifteen-strut three-layer diamond-pattern system* — to avoid confusion. An alternative is to add the prefix *expanded* to the names of diamond-pattern systems. Thus, the twelve-strut three-layer diamond-pattern system becomes the *expanded cuboctahedron* and the circuit-pattern figure simply the *cuboctahedron*.

A final point to note about these figures is that the struts form many different types of circuit, as in the cuboctahedron and in the following two examples.

Photograph 5 shows the circuit-pattern figure formed by joining the ends of the fifteen-strut three-layer diamond-pattern system. The struts form one continuous circuit, containing all fifteen struts, which weaves about without touching itself. The tendon network surrounding the struts defines the edges of a polyhedron with two pentagonal, five quadrilateral, and ten triangular faces, as shown in Diagram 4.7. Since the faces of such a polyhedron cannot all be regular, a decision must be made as to which faces, if any, are to be regular. Usually it is assumed that the two penta-

4.7

gonal faces are regular and that the Tensegrity system is symmetrically arranged about an axis which passes through their centres.

Photograph 6 shows the circuit-pattern figure derived from the twenty-strut four-layer diamond-pattern system. The struts form five square circuits which interweave without touching one another, while the tendon network surrounding them defines the edges of a polyhedron with two pentagonal, ten quadrilateral, and ten triangular faces, as in Diagram 4.8. As with the previous example, not all of these faces can be regular, and it is usually assumed that the pentagons are regular and that the figure is symmetrically arranged about an axis which passes through their centres.

4.8

Diamond-pattern Systems Derived from Circuit-pattern Systems

The process of evolving circuit-pattern systems from diamond-pattern systems can be reversed and diamond-pattern systems evolved from circuit-pattern systems. Diagram 4.9 shows how the edges of an icosidodecahedron can be forced apart to create a figure with the creased diamond shapes characteristic of diamond-pattern Tensegrity systems. In this sketch the edges represent the tendons of the system, and the struts occupy the creases in the diamonds. This can be done to the other figures described in this chapter, though it may be found that the strut ends of some of the larger figures will be so close together that it would be better to leave them as circuit-pattern figures.

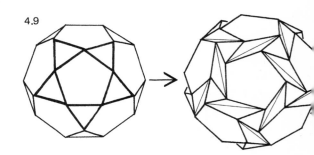

4.9

The Expanded Octahedron

In Chapter 2 it was stated that the figure often referred to as the Tensegrity icosahedron should more accurately be called the Tensegrity expanded octahedron. At that point little justification could be given for the name, though it was noted that the distances between the ends of the parallel struts were less than the lengths of the other tendons. Now that both the diamond- and circuit-pattern systems have been introduced, the name can be discussed in more detail.

If the expanded version of the icosidodecahedron, the diamond-pattern system represented by Diagram 4.9, is compressed and its strut ends joined, the circuit-pattern icosidodecahedron (Photograph 7), with its six interweaving pentagonal circuits of struts, is formed. Similarly, the circuit-pattern cuboctahedron (Photograph 4) can be formed by compressing the expanded cuboctahedron (Photograph 3) and joining its strut ends. If the figure under consideration (Photograph 1) is compressed, the two parts of each pair of struts move closer to one another; if their ends were joined, each pair could be replaced by a single strut. In the first two examples the struts were joined to form five-sided and three-sided polygons; in the third example they formed two-sided polygons. When the struts merge to form single struts, the tendons form the edges of the regular octahedron, hence the name *Tensegrity expanded octahedron*.

Final Notes

There are many other circuit-pattern systems, some of which are described in later chapters, but they all behave similarly. An important characteristic of all circuit-pattern figures not mentioned to date, is that they are enantiomorphic. In other words, there is a left-handed and a right-handed version of each figure, each version being the mirror image of the other, so care must be taken when this could be critical.

Finally, as has been mentioned, these figures are very much firmer and more stable than their diamond-pattern equivalents. This is one of the reasons why circuit-pattern figures are used so much in the applications discussed in Chapter 8.

5. Circuit-Pattern Systems Based on the Geodesic Polyhedra of R. Buckminster Fuller

Larger circuit-pattern systems must be based on larger polyhedra, such as the geodesic polyhedra developed by R. Buckminster Fuller. This discussion can only give a very general introduction to this type of polyhedron, but further information can be found in *Synergetics*, by R. Buckminster Fuller, or in *Polyhedra: A Visual Approach*, by A. J. Pugh.

The Generation of Geodesic Polyhedra

There are many different families of these polyhedra, but this description will only involve certain figures derived by the alternate method. In the alternate method, the geodesic polyhedron is derived from an existing polyhedron, called its principal polyhedron. The first step is to triangulate any faces of the principal polyhedron which are not already triangles. The sketches in Diagram 5.1 show the Platonic polyhedra, where the tetrahedron, the octahedron, and the icosahedron already have triangular faces, the cube has each of its square faces divided into four equal triangles, and the dodecahedron has each of its pentagonal faces divided into five equal triangles.

The edges of each triangle should be divided into equal numbers of equal parts and then lines drawn between the points established, to define a triangular grid on each face, as shown in Diagram 5.2. If the original triangles are equilateral, the smaller triangles will be equilateral, and if the original faces are isosceles triangles (like the triangles on the faces of the cube and the dodecahedron), the smaller triangles will be isosceles, too. Each subdivision is named

5.1

tetrahedron

octahedron

icosahedron

cube

dodecahedron

5.2

two frequency

three frequency

four frequency

five frequency

six frequency

according to its frequency (the number of parts into which each edge of the original face is subdivided). The diagram shows faces subdivided in from two to six frequencies, though much higher frequencies are possible.

The subdivided principal polyhedron, such as the icosahedron with its faces subdivided to three frequencies in Diagram 5.3a, should now be surrounded by an imaginary sphere — its circumsphere — which touches each of its vertices. Lines should be drawn from the centre of that sphere, through each place where lines intersect on the principal polyhedron, out to the surface of that sphere. The points defined by these lines on the surface of the sphere are the vertices of the geodesic polyhedron, and they should be joined by a set of straight lines reproducing the patterns sketched on the principal polyhedron, to define the edges of the figure. The obvious difference between a subdivided principal polyhedron (Diagram 5.3a) and its geodesic polyhedron (Diagram 5.3b) is that the latter figure is more spherical.

Geodesic Polyhedra and the Circuit Pattern

Since four tendons, defining four edges of a polyhedron, meet at each vertex of a circuit-pattern figure, and since six edges meet at most of the vertices of these geodesic polyhedra, it is difficult at first to see how circuit-pattern Tensegrity systems can be based on them. The difficulty is made worse by the fact that circuit-pattern Tensegrity figures cannot be based on all geodesic polyhedra. Fortunately, there are a few simple rules to clarify the issue.

Circuit-pattern Tensegrity systems can be based on any geodesic polyhedron derived by the alternate method, provided that the faces of the principal polyhedron have been subdivided to a frequency which is a multiple of two. The sketches in Diagram 5.4 show a triangular face of a principal polyhedron subdivided to various frequencies; the edges of the original triangles are shown in slightly heavier line than the lines which subdivide each face. Over each face appear, in very heavy line, the paths taken by the struts and tendons in the circuit-pattern figures. This pattern, a tessellation of hexagons and triangles, cannot be superimposed symmetrically over a face which has been subdivided to a frequency which

5.3

a

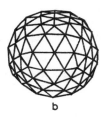

b

5.4

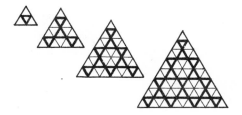

is not a multiple of two. Hexagons occur along the edges of the
original triangles, half on one triangle and half on the adjacent
triangle. The circuits may also define faces other than hexagons
and triangles about the vertices of the original triangles of the
principal polyhedron, as is apparent in the following examples.

Next, one must relate the individual struts and tendons to the
circuits established in Diagram 5.4. Diagram 5.5 shows the struts
and tendons sketched onto triangles of a principal polyhedron
divided to various frequencies. It can be seen that the struts and
the tendons follow the same lines as the circuits identified in
Diagram 5.4 and that the circuits of struts interweave one another,
just as they did in the systems described in Chapter 4.

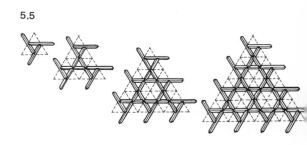

5.5

Examples

Having discussed the basic principles, it is worth studying a few
examples. The heavier lines in the following sketches show the
paths of the circuits of struts and tendons round the figure, and
the lighter lines show the edges generated by the edges of the
principal polyhedron (the icosahedron). The broken lines show the
other edges of the geodesic polyhedron.

The two-frequency icosahedron (Diagram 5.6) is the icosidodecahedron described in Chapter 4. The Tensegrity figure shown in
Photograph 6 has thirty struts which form six pentagonal interweaving circuits of struts and sixty tendons which define the
edges of an icosidodecahedron. All the struts of this figure can
be the same length, and all the tendons equal in length.

The figure based on the four-frequency icosahedron (Diagram
5.7) has 120 struts arranged in twelve interweaving decagonal
circuits, and 240 tendons, as shown in Photograph 10. Since
geodesic polyhedra are not as regular as the Archimedean polyhedra, this figure will usually have struts of two different lengths
and tendons of three different lengths. (Instructions for building a
model of this figure are given in Appendix 3.)

The figure based on the six-frequency icosahedron (Diagram
5.8) has 270 struts and 540 tendons as shown in Photograph 11.
It has eighteen circuits of struts which interweave without touch-

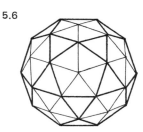

5.6

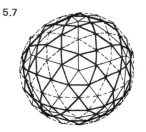

5.7

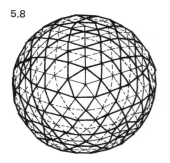

5.8

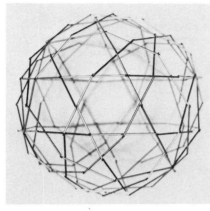

10. A four-frequency icosahedron

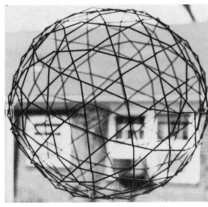

11. A six-frequency icosahedron
(circuit pattern)

ing one another. Each circuit contains fifteen struts, but there are
two different types of circuit, as there are usually struts of five
different lengths in two different sequences round the figure.
There are usually tendons of six different lengths. This figure can
be built in exactly the same way as the other circuit-pattern
figures, but it takes a very long time to build, simply because it
has so many components.

By now the basic idea should be apparent, and it is worth
looking briefly at a wider range of figures. The table in Diagram
5.9 gives the numbers of struts and tendons for the two-, four-,
six-, and eight-frequency Tensegrity figures derived from the
Platonic polyhedra and the truncated tetrahedron. The multi-
frequency polyhedra derived from the truncated tetrahedron are

NUMBERS OF STRUTS AND TENDONS FOR FIGURES BASED ON SOME GEODESIC POLYHEDRA					
Principal Polyhedra	Data for the Principal Polyhedra	Subdivision by the Alternate Method			
		2	4	6	8
tetrahedron	4 vertices 6 edges 4 triangular faces.	6 struts (struts double up) 12 tendons (octahedron)	24 struts 48 tendons	54 struts 108 tendons	96 struts 192 tendons
octahedron	6 vertices 12 edges 8 triangular faces.	12 struts 24 tendons (cuboctahedron)	48 struts 96 tendons	108 struts 216 tendons	192 struts 384 tendons
icosahedron	12 vertices 30 edges 20 triangular faces.	30 struts 60 tendons (icosidodeca--hedron)	120 struts 240 tendons	270 struts 540 tendons	480 struts 960 tendons
cube	8 vertices 12 edges 6 square or 24 triangular faces.	36 struts 72 tendons	144 struts 288 tendons	324 struts 648 tendons	576 struts 1152 tendons
dodecahedron	20 vertices 30 edges 12 pentagonal or 60 triangular faces	90 struts 180 tendons	360 struts 720 tendons	810 struts 1620 tendons	1440 struts 2880 tendons
truncated tetrahedron	12 vertices 18 edges 4 triangular and 4 hexagonal faces. or 28 triangular faces.	42 struts 84 tendons	168 struts 336 tendons	378 struts 756 tendons	672 struts 1344 tendons

created by dividing each hexagonal face into triangles and then subdividing each triangle into smaller triangles, as before. In the table it can be seen that there is an enormous difference in the numbers of struts and tendons from figure to figure. Even larger figures can be produced by subdividing the principal polyhedra to higher frequencies.

General Note on the Construction of Models

It takes a long time to build the larger examples of this type of figure, simply because of the numbers of struts and tendons involved. Fortunately, as much can be learned from the smaller figures, so instructions for the assembly of one large figure and two relatively small ones are given in Appendix 3. The large figure, the four-frequency icosahedron, has already been described. The two smaller figures are the two-frequency cube and the two-frequency truncated tetrahedron. The two-frequency cube (Photograph 12) has thirty-six struts and seventy-two tendons, the struts being arranged in six hexagonal circuits which undulate and interweave without touching one another. The tendons define a hexagon at each of the vertices of the principal polyhedron, and a square adjoined by four triangles for each of its six faces. The two-frequency truncated tetrahedron (Photograph 13) has forty-two struts and eighty-four tendons, the struts being arranged in seven hexagonal circuits which interweave without touching one another. The tendons define a pentagon at each vertex of the principal polyhedron, a hexagon for each of its four hexagonal faces, and twenty-eight triangles.

Final Notes

There are enormous numbers of geodesic polyhedra on which circuit-pattern Tensegrity systems can be based. This discussion has only described a few systems based on figures derived by the alternate method from a few principal polyhedra, but there are many other ways of subdividing principal polyhedra, and there are many other polyhedra which can be used as principal polyhedra.

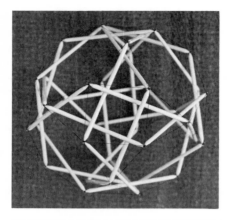

12. A two-frequency cube

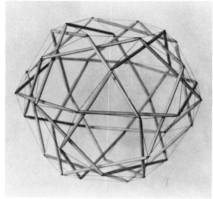

13. A two-frequency truncated
tetrahedron

In addition these circuit-pattern Tensegrity systems are not regular,
and many variations can be made in the geometry of each figure. It
is hoped that this chapter, together with the assembly instructions
in Appendix 3, explain enough of the basic ideas and techniques
to allow the reader to work on other figures of this type.

6. The Zigzag Pattern

Six tendons can be added to the expanded octahedron (Photograph 1) to join the ends of parallel struts and define the shorter axis of each diamond of tendons, as in Diagram 6.1a. Then opposite pairs of tendons can be removed from each diamond of tendons so that three tendons form a Z shape, or its mirror image, between the ends of each strut, as in Diagram 6.1b. When removing the tendons, it is important that all of the Z-type arrangements that are left are the same, and mirror-image versions are not mixed up in the same model. The tendons now form the edges of a slightly distorted truncated tetrahedron. The struts do not touch one another, but they are no longer parallel, as can be seen in Photograph 14.

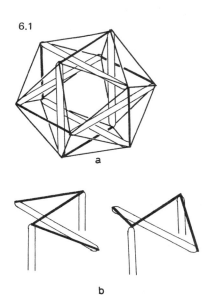

6.1

a

b

Some Characteristics of Zigzag-pattern Figures

The truncated tetrahedron is a typical example of a large family of figures, all of which have their tendons arranged in Z shapes (or their mirror images) between the ends of each strut, hence the name *zigzag pattern*. In the larger figures the Z arrangements are so shallow that they are almost straight lines, but it was still felt that the name *zigzag* was apt for this type of figure.

In common with the structure of nearly every other zigzag figure, the struts of the truncated tetrahedron do not touch one another and are surrounded by a network of tendons. If one of the tendons of this figure is plucked, the figure will vibrate readily, but such vibrations can be eliminated from zigzag-pattern figures by the addition of further tendons.

Another characteristic of this type of figure which can be seen in the truncated tetrahedron is that they are enantiomorphic (that is, there are two versions of each figure, each version being

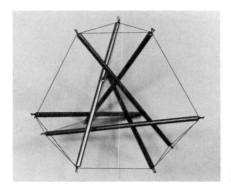

14. A truncated tetrahedron

the mirror image of the other), and care must be exercised when this is a critical consideration.

Since the tendons of the truncated tetrahedron defined the edges of a distorted polyhedron, it would be reasonable to expect that zigzag-pattern figures could be based on other polyhedra. Since three tendons meet at the end of each strut and those tendons define the edges of the polyhedron, it would appear that the most likely polyhedra to consider would be those with 3 edges meeting at each vertex.

Zigzag-Pattern Systems Based on Platonic Polyhedra

The centre and left-hand sketches in Diagram 6.2 show zigzag pattern figures based on the octahedron and the cube, but there is a lot of interaction between their struts. The ten struts of the dodecahedron in the right-hand sketch do not touch one another, but that figure is only symmetrical about a single axis passing through one pair of opposite pentagons of tendons, and one would expect a figure based on a regular polyhedron to be symmetrical about axes drawn through any opposite pair of faces.

6.2

 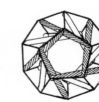

Zigzag-Pattern Systems Based on
Archimedean Polyhedra

No fewer than seven of the thirteen Archimedean polyhedra have three edges meeting at each vertex, and each of the seven forms the basis of a Tensegrity system. Each of the figures has struts all the same length and tendons of one size. Instructions for assembling each of the figures appear in Appendix 4, including a way of building the truncated tetrahedron which is quicker than the way described at the beginning of this chapter. Since all of these figures have similar characteristics and since the larger figures take longer to build, many readers will decide to build only the smaller ones.

The figure based on the *truncated tetrahedron* (Photograph 14) has six struts and eighteen tendons, with the tendons defining the edges of a distorted truncated tetrahedron (Diagram 6.3). The triangles of tendons are undistorted, as the struts approach each of their vertices from the same angle, but the struts approach the vertices of the hexagons from two angles, causing them to distort slightly.

The figure based on the *truncated octahedron* (Diagram 6.4a) has twelve struts and thirty-six tendons, the tendons defining the edges of a distorted truncated octahedron. The squares of tendons are undistorted, as the struts approach each vertex at the same angle; but the hexagons are twisted into almost triangular shapes, as the struts meet them at two angles. If the tendons are not tied too tightly, three tendons can be added to each distorted hexagon, as shown in Diagram 6.4b, to divide it into four equilateral triangles. The tendons now define the edges of a *snub cube* (Diagram 6.4c and Photograph 15). The truncated octahedron vibrates readily when one of its tendons is plucked, but once the extra tendons are added to create a snub cube, the figure will no longer vibrate.

The figure shown in Photograph 16 is based on the *truncated cube* (Diagram 6.5), has twelve struts and thirty-six tendons, the tendons defining the edges of a distorted truncated cube. The triangles of tendons are undistorted, but the struts approach the octagons from two different angles, and distort the octagons into approximately square shapes. This distortion of the

6.3

6.4

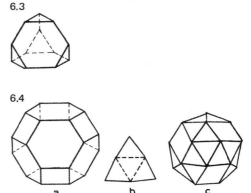

a   b   c

6.5

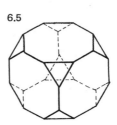

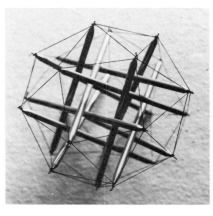

15. A snub cube (zigzag pattern)

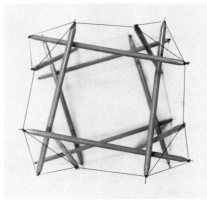

16. A truncated cube

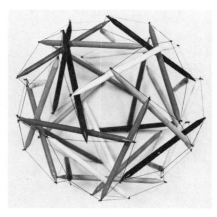

17. A truncated icosahedron

octagonal faces is equivalent to the distortion of the hexagonal faces, of the truncated tetrahedron and truncated octahedron.

The figure shown in Photograph 17 is based on the *truncated isocahedron* (Diagram 6.6a), has thirty struts and ninety tendons, the tendons defining the edges of a distorted truncated icosahedron. The distortion is caused by the struts approaching the hexagonal faces at two different angles and forcing them into approximately triangular shapes. All of the struts approach the pentagonal faces at similar angles, so they do not distort. Three extra tendons can be added to each distorted hexagonal face, as shown in Diagram 6.6b, to divide it into four equilateral triangles. This will create a tendon network which defines all of the edges of a *snub dodecahedron*. The tendons need not be added for the sake of stability, though they will prevent the figure from vibrating.

An interesting model of the truncated icosahedron can be built with struts of five different colours, six struts in each colour. The five colours can be distributed symmetrically over the figure if they are placed so that three struts of similar colour form the three vertices of each hexagon, as indicated in Diagram 6.7. If this is done correctly and the struts extended in one's imagination, it will be found that each set of struts of one colour defines part of the edges of a regular tetrahedron.

If the model is built with rubber-band tendons, struts of similar colour can be joined, end to end as shown in Diagram 6.8, to define the edges of five tetrahedra which do not touch one another (unless the struts are very thick). The tendons now define the edges of a regular dodecahedron. The figure now represents a well-known polyhedron which is a compound of five regular tetrahedra whose vertices define the vertices of a regular dodecahedron.

Like the truncated icosahedron, the *truncated dodecahedron* (Photograph 18) has thirty struts and ninety tendons, but the tendons of this figure define the edges of a distorted truncated dodecahedron (Diagram 6.9). The triangular faces defined by the tendons are undistorted, but the struts approach the decagonal faces from two angles of inclination and cause them to form approximately pentagonal shapes.

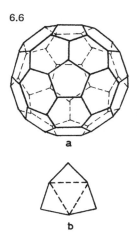

6.6

a

b

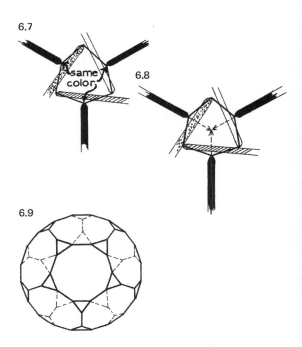

6.7

same color

6.8

6.9

18. A truncated dodecahedron

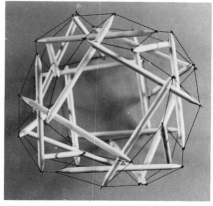

19. A great rhombicuboctahedron

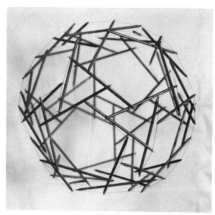

20. A great rhombicosidodecahedron

The figure shown in Photograph 19 is based on the *great rhombicuboctahedron* (Diagram 6.10), has twenty-four struts and seventy-two tendons, the tendons defining the edges of a distorted great rhombicuboctahedron. All of the faces of the original polyhedron are distorted in this figure because the struts approach each face from two angles. The square faces assume rhombic shapes, the hexagons are almost triangular, and the octagons are almost square.

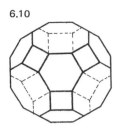

6.10

The Tensegrity system based on the *great rhombicosidodecahedron* (Diagram 6.11) and shown in Photograph 20 has sixty struts and 180 tendons, the tendons defining the edges of a distorted great rhombicosidodecahedron. This is the largest zigzag system based on an Archimedean polyhedron, though it has similar characteristics to those of the smaller figures described earlier in this chapter. As with the great rhombicuboctahedron, each face of this figure is distorted because the struts approach them from two angles. The square faces become rhombic, the hexagonal faces become almost triangular, and the decagonal faces take on pentagonal shapes.

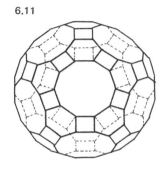

6.11

General Notes on the Distortion of Faces

Most of the zigzag figures described so far have had some or all of their faces distorted. The explanation was that these distortions were caused by the struts approaching the faces from two different angles. But another explanation is to compare these figures to a balloon, with their struts pushing outwards like the air inside the balloon and their tendons pulling inwards like the skin of the balloon. The tendons, like the skin of the balloon, try to force the figure into the smallest volume the struts will permit, causing its faces to distort. It is possible to predict which faces will distort by sketching the struts on a drawing or a model of the polyhedron.

Triangles of tendons are always undistorted, even though they may not be equilateral. Sometimes square faces are undistorted (Diagram 6.12a) like those of the truncated octahedron, and sometimes they assume rhombic shapes (Diagram 6.12b) like those of the great rhombicuboctahedron.

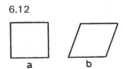

6.12

a   b

Pentagons (Diagram 6.13a) do not distort, though they may not be regular at the start. All of the hexagons encountered so far in this book have been distorted as shown in Diagram 6.13b because the struts approach their vertices from two different angles, but some undistorted hexagons (Diagram 6.13c) with all struts approaching vertices at similar angles appear in figures described later.

Octagons and decagons always distort into approximately square and pentagonal shapes, as in Diagram 6.14, because the struts approach each face from two different angles.

There are two reactions to the distortion of faces. The first is to accept that the figure has taken up its most natural, most efficient form and should not be changed. On the other hand, a distorted shape may be unacceptable in certain situations, in which case extra tendons must be added to prevent the distortions. The extra tendons must be added carefully, as they can be added in such a way that they have no effect on the distortion. Various effective ways of adding tendons are illustrated in Diagram 6.15.

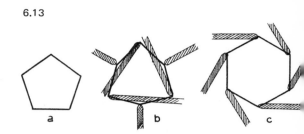

6.13

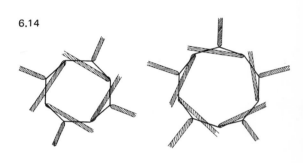

6.14

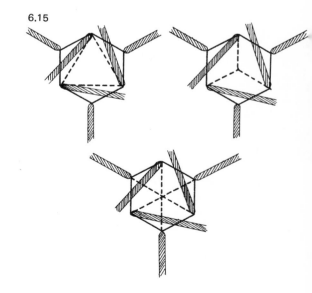

6.15

Figures Having Similar Numbers of Struts and Tendons

The truncated octahedron and the truncated cube have the same numbers of struts and tendons as one another; yet the truncated octahedron seems a lot sturdier than the truncated cube. Similarly, the truncated icosahedron and the truncated dodecahedron have equal numbers of struts and tendons, yet the truncated icosahedron seems sturdier than the truncated dodecahedron. This is because the faces of the sturdier figures are more balanced than the faces of the other figures. In other words, there is a bigger difference in size between the octagonal and the triangular faces of the truncated cube than there is between the hexagonal and the square faces of the truncated octahedron. Similarly, there is a bigger difference in size between the decagonal and the triangular faces of the truncated dodecahedron than there is between the hexagonal and the pentagonal faces of the truncated icosahedron.

Figures Based on the Geodesic Polyhedra
of R. Buckminster Fuller

Zigzag systems can be based on the geodesic polyhedra described
in Chapter 5. Diagram 6.16 shows a four-frequency icosahedron,
but at first it is difficult to relate struts and tendons to such a
figure, as six edges meet at most of its vertices, whereas only
three tendons meet at each strut end of most zigzag-pattern
Tensegrity systems.

Fortunately, grids of lines can be superimposed over some of
these polyhedra to emphasize those edges which define the tendon
networks of zigzag-pattern systems. The sketches in Diagram 6.17
show grids superimposed on triangles that have been subdivided
to various frequencies. The grids are essentially tessellations of
hexagons, though different polygons are formed about certain
vertices of the main triangles, as later examples demonstrate. The
grids can only be superimposed over figures which have been
subdivided to frequencies which are multiples of three, so zigzag-
pattern systems cannot be based on figures subdivided to other
frequencies.

The sketches in Diagram 6.18 show how struts can be related to
those tendon networks. It can be seen how symmetrically they are
arranged against each triangle of the principal polyhedron. It can
also be seen how the struts cut across some hexagons, yet radiate
from others. In the former case, the struts are approaching from
two different angles and make the hexagons distort like the
hexagonal faces of figures based on the Archimedean polyhedra.
In the latter case, the struts approach from similar angles, and the
hexagons do not distort.

The table in Diagram 6.19 gives the numbers of struts and
tendons for Tensegrity figures based on the geodesic polyhedra
derived from the three-, six-, nine-, and twelve-frequency subdi-
visions of the Platonic polyhedra and the truncated tetrahedron.
It can be seen that the three-frequency figures based on the tetrahedron, the octahedron, and the icosahedron are Archimedean
polyhedra, which have been described earlier in this chapter. The
numbers of struts and tendons vary greatly from figure to figure
and even larger numbers of components are found in higher

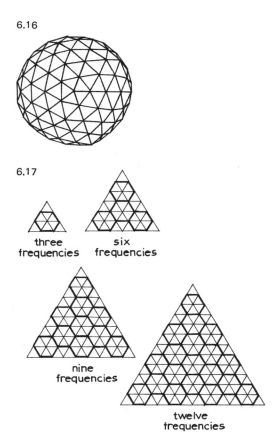

6.16

6.17

three
frequencies

six
frequencies

nine
frequencies

twelve
frequencies

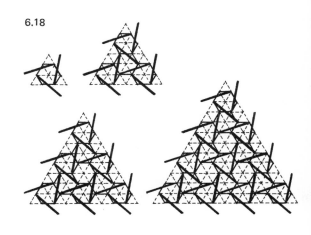

6.18

NUMBERS OF STRUTS AND TENDONS FOR FIGURES BASED ON SOME GEODESIC POLYHEDRA					
Principal Polyhedra	Data for the Principal Polyhedra	Subdivision by the Alternate Method			
		3	6	9	12
tetrahedron	4 vertices 6 edges 4 triangular faces.	6 struts 18 tendons (truncated tetrahedron)	24 struts 72 tendons	54 struts 162 tendons	96 struts 288 tendons
octahedron	6 vertices 12 edges 8 triangular faces.	12 struts 36 tendons (truncated octahedron)	48 struts 144 tendons	108 struts 324 tendons	192 struts 576 tendons
icosahedron	12 vertices 30 edges 20 triangular faces.	30 struts 90 tendons (truncated icosahedron)	120 struts 360 tendons	270 struts 810 tendons	480 struts 1440 tendons
cube	8 vertices 12 edges 6 square or 24 triangular faces	36 struts 108 tendons	144 struts 432 tendons	324 struts 972 tendons	576 struts 1728 tendons
dodecahedron	20 vertices 30 edges 12 pentagonal or 60 triangular faces.	90 struts 270 tendons	360 struts 1080 tendons	810 struts 2430 tendons	1440 struts 4320 tendons
truncated tetrahedron	12 vertices 18 edges 4 triangular and 4 hexagonal faces or 28 triangular faces	42 struts 126 tendons	168 struts 504 tendons	378 struts 1134 tendons	672 struts 2016 tendons

frequency figures. Similarities may be noticed between the numbers of struts in this table and in the figures described in Diagram 5.9, a point which will be discussed in Chapter 7.

Examples

The first example (Photograph 21) is the figure based on the three-frequency dodecahedron. It has ninety struts, and its 270 tendons define twelve pentagons and eighty hexagons, twenty of which are undistorted.

The second example (Photograph 22) is based on the six-frequency octahedron. It has forty-eight struts, and its 144 tendons define six squares and forty-four hexagons, twelve of which are undistorted.

The third example (Photograph 23) is based on the three-frequency truncated tetrahedron. It has forty-two struts, and its 126 tendons define twelve pentagons and thirty-two hexagons, four of which are undistorted.

Instructions for assembling all three figures can be found in Appendix 4. However, it should be remembered that the more struts a figure has, the longer it will take to build. It should also be remembered that the tendons of a large figure must be tied very tightly if it is not to sag from the weight of its struts. All zigzag figures based on geodesic polyhedra behave in ways similar to those of the smaller figures described earlier in this chapter.

An Interesting Characteristic of
Zigzag-Pattern Systems

Three tendons and one strut meet at each vertex of a zigzag system, and since each component has two ends, there are twice as many components as there are junctions of them. In theory, any structure with pinned joints like these structures must have a minimum of $3J - 6$ components, where J is the number of junctions, if it is to be simply stiff. So the larger zigzag systems have approximately two-thirds the number of components they ought to have. It will have been noticed that zigzag-pattern systems vibrate when a tendon is plucked. In other words, loads

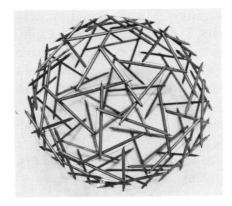

21. A three-frequency dodecahedron

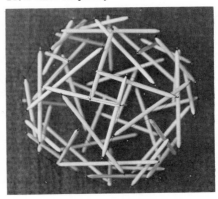

22. A six-frequency octahedron
(zigzag pattern)

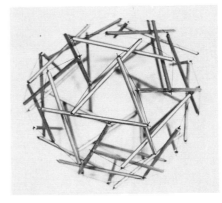

23. A three-frequency truncated
tetrahedron

are transferred throughout the system with little dampening at the joints. Such vibration can be eliminated by adding extra tendons, as when the snub cube and the snub dodecahedron were created by adding tendons to the truncated octahedron and the truncated icosahedron. When tendons are added to prevent a figure distorting, they also prevent it vibrating. But if distorted faces are acceptable, the tendons can be added as shown in Diagram 6.20. It is interesting to note that once enough extra tendons have been added to prevent vibration, the figure often has exactly $3J - 6$ members.

6.20

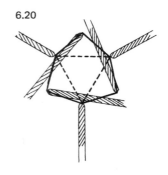

7. Further Tensegrity Systems (all patterns)

By now it may be apparent that there are more Tensegrity systems than could be described in one volume. This chapter describes various methods by which further systems can be evolved, and gives brief descriptions of a few families of figures which have not been mentioned previously. It is hoped that this discussion will enable readers to find starting points for their own researches.

Four Methods of Evolving New
Tensegrity Systems

One way of evolving new figures is to postulate a *new concept of Tensegrity* or to modify an existing concept. For example, it might be possible to find a different interpretation of the soap-bubble analogy. The resulting figures might be very different from the figures described here so far.

A second method is to discover a *new relationship* between struts and tendons. There are several ways of doing this, as will be suggested later.

A third method (dealt with in more detail later on) is to discover or develop *new polyhedral figures* which can be used as bases for Tensegrity systems using an already established relationship between struts and tendons.

A fourth method is to *extend an existing idea or figure*. This method has already been used, especially in Chapter 3. One of the most promising types of figure to try to extend are the simple systems described in Chapter 2.

New Relationships Between Struts and Tendons

There are several ways of discovering new relationships between struts and tendons, the first being to interpret the relationship between the struts and tendons of an existing figure in a different way. For example, the expanded octahedron in Diagram 7.1 could be regarded as a figure composed of six struts, each of which is surrounded by a diamond arrangement of tendons. Alternatively, the same system could be regarded as a figure composed of 6 struts which are contained by eight triangles of tendons. Though this new description of the relationship between the components does not produce further figures in this case, it does illustrate the general idea. The simple systems described in Chapter 2 are figures from which such new interpretations which could lead to the discovery of further figures could be made.

Another method of evolving a new relationship between struts and tendons is to manipulate the struts and tendons of an existing figure until a new pattern is produced. A good example of this method appears at the beginning of Chapter 6, where the truncated tetrahedron, with its zigzag arrangement of struts and tendons, is evolved from the expanded octahedron, with its diamond patterns of struts and tendons.

A third method of evolving a new relationship is through discovering an entirely new figure. Visualizing and building such a figure may not be easy, especially if it has many struts and tendons. One of the most profitable areas for this sort of investigation would be among the simple systems described in Chapter 2, as smaller figures are easier to visualize and build.

A final approach is to consider the various ways in which struts and tendons can be related to each other. For example, most of the systems described so far have had a strut on either side of each strut. In the diamond-pattern systems, they were directly opposite one another, and in the zigzag-pattern systems they were staggered, as in Diagram 7.2a, b. Since there must be a strut end on either side of each strut, so that its tendons can be fixed to something, the only other possibility would appear to be to have more than one strut on one or both sides, as in Diagram 7.2c.

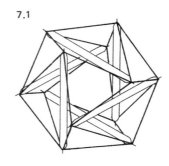

7.1

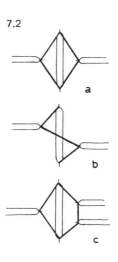

7.2

a

b

c

One potential drawback with such an arrangement is that it might be possible to replace the pair of struts with a single strut and thus end up with one of the arrangements already described.

All the relationships shown so far have had single struts suspended in space or joined end-to-end in circuits. Other relationships could be established by joining more than two strut ends together and then creating stable configurations by adding components. Diagram 7.3 shows a series of struts forming a grid of hexagons. A mast runs through the centre of each hexagon, and tendons are added to stabilize the whole assembly. Purists may not regard this type of structure as a true Tensegrity system.

7.3

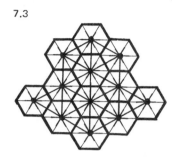

Basing Tensegrity Systems
on Other Polyhedra

Perhaps the easiest way of evolving further Tensegrity systems is to find additional polyhedra which can be used as bases for such figures. Further polyhedra often are found in various publications or evolved from one's own studies. In the latter case, a background knowledge of polyhedra is invaluable.

To determine whether a given polyhedron can form the basis of a Tensegrity system, the first job is to find a suitable arrangement of struts and tendons for it by sketching the components over a drawing — or preferably a model — of that polyhedron. The usual sequence is to look for the symmetries of the figure, then to trace a suitable network of tendons over the figure, and finally to sketch on the struts. It may not be possible to arrive at a suitable arrangement until several attempts have been made, and there may, of course, be no possible arrangement at all. There is also the possibility that a figure has a relationship between struts and tendons which has not been described in this book. Once a suitable arrangement has been found, a cardboard model can be used to work out an assembly sequence and, in some cases, for determining the relative lengths of components.

Before actually building the Tensegrity figure, it is worth checking to see that it is not a simpler figure which has already been discovered by a more direct approach. It can be very frustrating to finish a model, expecting it to be an original one, only to discover it has been built already.

Just because a Tensegrity system appears to work on paper is no guarantee that it will be stable when it is constructed from struts and tendons, and some figures will inevitably be disappointments. However, it is always worth studying such figures carefully to see what can be learned from them.

Examples

The polyhedra shown in Diagram 7.4 were derived from the truncated octahedron by removing the portions of that figure about each vertex. The lighter lines show the edges of the truncated octahedron, and the heavier lines show the edges of the polyhedra produced from it. In Diagram 7.4a only a small amount has been removed; in Diagram 7.4b a bit more has been removed, so that the vertices of the new figure define the midpoints of the edges of the truncated octahedron. In Diagram 7.4c even more of the figure has been removed.

The first of the polyhedra has eight twelve-sided faces, six octagonal faces, and twenty-four triangular faces. It has three edges meeting at each vertex, so it is worth seeing if a zigzag-pattern arrangement of struts and tendons can be based on it. If the edges of the polyhedron define the tendon network, thirty-six struts can be added (Diagram 7.5), to produce a Tensegrity system. From that diagram it can be predicted that the twelve-sided and eight-sided faces defined by the tendons will distort and the triangles will remain undistorted.

The second polyhedron (Diagram 7.6) has 8 hexagonal faces, six square faces, and 24 triangular faces. Four edges meet at each vertex of this figure, and it will be found that the figure can be used as the basis of a circuit-pattern system with thirty-six struts and seventy-two tendons.

The third polyhedron (Diagram 7.7) has 6 square faces and thirty-two hexagonal faces. Three edges meet at each vertex, and if those edges define a network of tendons, thirty-six struts can be arranged within the network, as in the diagram, to define a zigzag-pattern Tensegrity system. From Diagram 7.7 it can be predicted

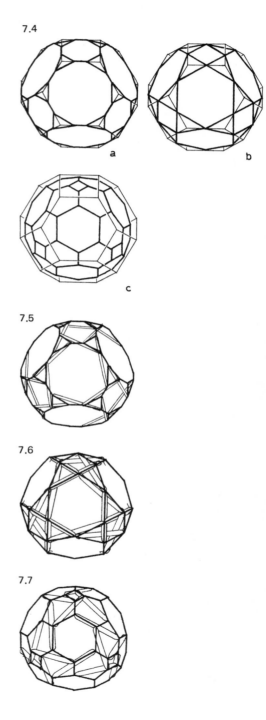

7.4

a b

c

7.5

7.6

7.7

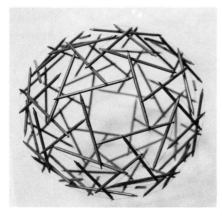

24. An 84-strut zigzag-pattern figure

that the six square faces and eight of the hexagonal faces will not distort and that the rest of the hexagonal faces will distort.

The final example (Diagram 7.8) is a slightly more complex polyhedron. The figure was created by triangulating each of the hexagonal faces of a truncated octahedron (a) and then projecting the centres of each hexagon onto the circumscribing sphere (b). The portions about each vertex were then removed to produce the figure shown in Diagram 7.8c. Since three edges meet at each vertex of that figure, it would appear that the edges could define a network of tendons belonging to a figure whose components are arranged in a zigzag pattern. Struts can be related to that network (d), and the resulting Tensegrity system (shown in Photograph 24) will have eighty-four struts and 252 tendons.

Tensegrity Systems and the Duals of the Archimedean Polyhedra

Readers familiar with the various families of polyhedra may have noticed that no mention has been made of the duals of the Archimedean polyhedra. The problem with those polyhedra is that none of them has the same number of edges meeting at each of its vertices, making it difficult to relate any of the three basic Tensegrity patterns to them. The example shown in Diagram 7.9 is the triakis icosahedron, which has three edges meeting at some of its vertices and ten at others.

7.8

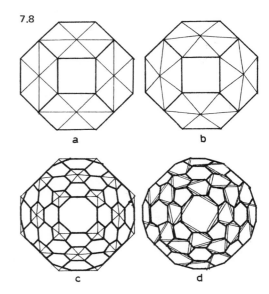

a b

c d

7.9

A Relationship Between Circuit-Pattern and Zigzag-Pattern Tensegrity Systems

Some readers may have noticed that more zigzag figures than circuit-pattern figures were based on the Archimedean polyhedra. They may also have noticed that some zigzag-pattern Tensegrity systems have the same number of struts. For example, both the truncated cube and the truncated octahedron have twelve struts each, and both the truncated icosahedron and the truncated dodecahedron have thirty struts each. Furthermore, they may have noticed the circuit-pattern cuboctahedron has twelve struts and the circuit-pattern icosidodecahedron has thirty struts. All three figures with twelve struts each are interrelated, as are the three figures with thirty struts each, as follows.

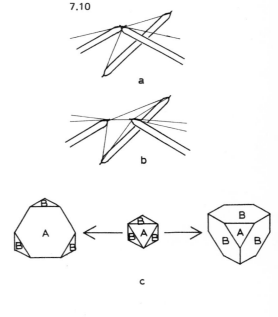

7.10

If the joined strut ends of a circuit-pattern cuboctahedron (Diagram 7.10a) are pulled apart, three extra tendons can be added between each pair of strut ends, to form a diamond pattern of tendons whose shorter axis is defined by a fifth tendon (Diagram 7.10b). At the beginning of Chapter 6 a similar arrangement of tendons was formed about each pair of strut ends belonging to an expanded octahedron. When a pair of tendons that formed opposite sides of a diamond shape were removed from each pair of strut ends, the zigzag-pattern truncated tetrahedron was formed. To make the transition from octahedron to truncated tetrahedron, four of the triangular faces of the former figure become hexagons (polygons with twice as many edges). Removing one set of pairs of tendons, say, to produce Z arrangements of tendons, makes one set of triangles into hexagons. Removing the other pair of tendons, instead, to produce reverse Z arrangements of tendons, changes the other set of triangles into hexagons, as shown by faces *A* and *B*, Diagram 7.10c.

Since all the faces of the octahedron are triangles, the same figure, the truncated tetrahedron, is produced, no matter which set of faces is expanded. But with a figure like the cuboctahedron, which has a set of triangular faces and a set of square faces, different polyhedra are produced, depending on whether Z or reversed Z arrangements of tendons are made (Diagram 7.11). The one arrangement will have the effect of expanding the square

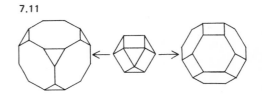

7.11

faces to produce a truncated cube, and the other, of expanding the triangular faces to produce a truncated octahedron, as shown. Thus, the two zigzag Tensegrity figures and the circuit-pattern figure are related.

Similarly, if the strut ends of a circuit-pattern icosidodecahedron are pulled apart, extra tendons added, and then some tendons removed to form Z or reversed Z arrangements of tendons, this will have the effect either of expanding the pentagonal faces to create a truncated dodecahedron or of expanding the triangular faces to create a truncated icosahedron, as shown in Diagram 7.12. So, again, there is a relationship between both of the zigzag figures and the circuit-pattern figure.

Among the zigzag-pattern figures based on the Archimedean polyhedra, there is only one having twenty-four struts — the great rhombicuboctahedron, and only one has sixty struts — the great rhombicosidodecahedron. The zigzag-pattern great rhombicuboctahedron can be evolved by pulling apart the ends of a circuit-pattern small rhombicuboctahedron, adding extra tendons, then removing some of them. In creating the zigzag-pattern figure, six of the squares of the small rhombicuboctoctahedron become octagons, and eight of its triangular faces become hexagons (Diagram 7.13). However, a different figure (Photograph 25) can be created if the other pairs of tendons are removed, instead. This has the effect of leaving the 6 squares and eight triangles as they are, and expanding the other twelve squares into octagons, as shown in Diagram 7.13. Similarly, a sixty-strut figure which is different from the great rhombicosidodecahedron can be evolved from the small rhombicosidodecahedron.

In chapter 6 it was noted that many of the zigzag-pattern systems based on geodesic polyhedra had the same number of struts as some of the circuit-pattern systems based on different geodesic figures. The zigzag-pattern figures could have been created from the circuit-pattern figures, by pulling apart the strut ends and then adding and removing tendons, as before. In effect, this is equivalent to expanding each triangle on the circuit pattern to form hexagons, with the original hexagons remaining hexagons. But if the zigzags were formed the other way, the effect would be

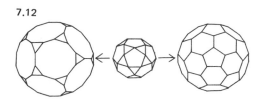

7.12

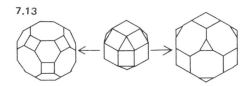

7.13

25. A 24-strut zigzag-pattern figure

to leave the triangles as they were and to expand the hexagons into twelve-sided polygons. The letters on the sketches in Diagram 7.14 show how the polygons are expanded. Unfortunately, the zigzag-pattern systems with these twelve-sided faces are not as sturdy as the ones with hexagonal faces.

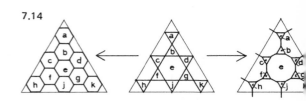

7.14

Cylindrical Tensegrity Systems

Since Tensegrity systems can be likened to balloons and soap bubbles, the figures described so far have been approximately spherical, which is the shape of the structurally more efficient balloons and of soap bubbles in free space. But it is also possible to build Tensegrity systems which are not spherical, as illustrated by the multilayer systems described in Chapters 3 and 4. Those figures could be regarded as being approximately cylindrical, though they narrow slightly at their tops and bottoms.

First, consider the twenty-strut four-layer circuit-pattern system shown in Photograph 6 and described in Chapter 4. Diagram 7.15a is a simplified net diagram of the polyhedron which is shown in Diagram 7.15b. In reality, there would be many small sinuses, or small gaps, between the faces of the net diagram, but they have been omitted, to simplify and clarify the diagram. It can be seen that this figure has two pentagonal ends and has sets of squares and triangles round the sides. Figures which could be used as bases for taller systems would have further layers of squares, and figures with larger diameters would have more squares and triangles round the sides and larger polygons at either end, as shown in the other simplified net diagrams (Diagrams 7.15c,d). It can be seen that the sides of these figures are tessellations of squares.

Two other tessellations which have four edges meeting at each vertex and which can be used as bases for cylindrical circuit-pattern systems are shown in Diagram 7.16. The ends in the left-hand tessellation can simply be polygons, but a ring of squares and triangles must be placed between the tessellation and the end polygons of the right-hand tessellation, as indicated by the dotted lines. This ensures that four edges meet at every

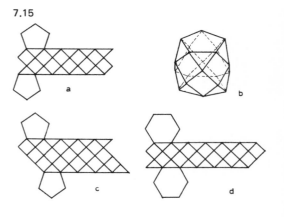

7.15

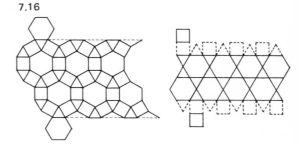

7.16

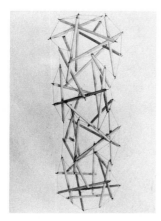

26. A cylindrical zigzag-pattern figure

vertex, allowing the circuits of struts to interweave in the Tensegrity systems.

Four tessellations can be used as bases for cylindrical zigzag systems. The top two shown in Diagram 7.17 incorporate twelve-sided polygons, so the Tensegrity systems based on them are not very strong. The tessellation shown at lower left in Diagram 7.17 consists of squares and octagons, and much stronger cylindrical zigzag systems can be based on it. The lower right-hand tessellation consists of hexagons and will be used as the next example. In these four sketches the dotted lines indicate the tops and bottoms of the cylinders. It can be seen that various polygons are needed to "fill in" between the sides and the ends of the figures.

Diagram 7.18 shows the simplified net diagram for the figure that appears in Photograph 26. The edges of this figure define a network of tendons, to which can be related a series of struts, shown in heavier lines the the diagram. All the faces are hexagonal, except for a few quadrilaterals between the sides and the ends of the figure. From the photograph it is obvious that this is a long, thin figure, very different in shape from the approximately spherical ones described earlier. Despite its shape, this figure is surprisingly rigid. It can be built by starting at one end and adding components systematically till it is complete, just like the other zigzag figures described in Appendix 4.

7.17

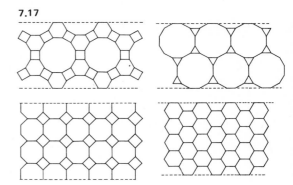

7.18

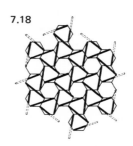

8. Applications of Tensegrity, Joining Systems Together, and the Construction of Larger Figures

Though the title of this chapter might suggest an assortment of topics, each is a factor in the consideration of the uses of Tensegrity. Tensegrity systems are usually joined together with some definite objective or application in mind. When building larger figures, one usually is thinking of them in a structural context.

Tensegrity systems are so fascinating that one instinctively feels they must be significant, even if it may be difficult to predict their most important applications. The author's background in architecture has resulted in the use of such words as *strut, tendon, structure*, and so on, but it should be appreciated that for some applications of Tensegrity such words could be inappropriate. The major importance of Tensegrity may be not for structures but for something entirely different, such as philosophy or as a valuable exercise in three dimensions. It is hoped that this volume will allow people from a variety of backgrounds to become familiar with Tensegrity systems and to form their own opinions on them from information gained by handling the models firsthand.

Structural Characteristics of Tensegrity Systems

Before any applications are suggested, it is worth considering those characteristics which are significant in a practical context. For example, the following characteristics would be significant if a system were being considered as a basis for a large-scale structure:

1. A Tensegrity system is a comprehensive force system and does not need external forces, such as those supplied by gravity or anchorages, to keep its components in the correct relationship to one another. Hence, a structure based on a Tensegrity system could be very useful in situations where it would be difficult to use other types of structure.

2. A Tensegrity system is merely a set of forces, though there is a temptation to think of these systems in terms of the struts and tendons of the models. Provided the components of a structure can cope with those forces, it does not matter what shape the components are or what material is used in their construction. Some Tensegrity-system structures may not look very much like the stick-and-string models, as is demonstrated by some of the larger figures described later in this chapter.

3. If a structure is built from struts and tendons, the connections between its components can be simple pinned joints, which makes the design and calculation of these figures relatively simple.

4. All the major forces in a Tensegrity system travel axially down the individual struts and tendons, so those components are taking load in the most efficient way.

5. Many of the figures vibrate readily, which means they are transferring loads very rapidly, preventing the loads from becoming localized. This could be an advantage in some situations, though in cases where vibrations would be a disadvantage, extra tendons could be added to prevent them.

It may be possible to introduce other significant characteristics, but they would depend on the application, the materials, and the design being contemplated. The characteristics listed here are significant in a structural context, but it might be necessary to draw up a very different list for another application of the idea of Tensegrity.

Joining Tensegrity Systems

Many of the systems described earlier are based on polyhedra, so they can be joined together in the same general formations as those polyhedra. Ideas can often be tested relatively quickly by joining cardboard models of the polyhedra instead of the Tensegrity systems themselves, provided allowances are made for the distortion of the faces in the Tensegrity systems. Tensegrity systems can either be joined so that the strut ends of one system touch the strut ends of adjacent figures or so that they do not. Obviously, the former way of joining them will tend to produce arrangements which are more rigid. In either case, it may be necessary to add tendons in order to stabilize the assembly. Once a set of figures has been joined, it may be possible to simplify the assembly by removing or replacing various components.

Both polyhedra and Tensegrity systems can be joined in any of three ways:

1. as a conglomeration of figures whose volumes or surfaces relate to one another in a special way, such as an arrangement looking like a cluster of soap bubbles;
2. as a long, slender structure such as a mast or a truss; and
3. as a grid or skeletal type of structure.

The conglomerations of Tensegrity systems (1) are the hardest to arrange because of the distortions and enantiomorphism of the individual figures. The long, slender structures (2) are much easier to design. They tend to be stronger than the long, cylindrical figures described in Chapter 7.

The grids and skeletal arrangements (3) are the most interesting. It is best to use the smaller, simpler systems for these arrangements, as so many figures will be required. In some cases, some of the Tensegrity figures can be omitted from the assembly, producing voids between the figures, as is shown in some of the following examples.

Three-strut octahedra (Diagram 8.1a) can be joined together, edge to edge, like the octahedra of the close-packing arrangement of octahedra and tetrahedra in Diagram 8.1b. The octahedra can be arranged in a single layer or in several layers. Extra tendons are not usually needed to stabilize the arrangement. Some of the octahedra can be omitted, especially in the multilayer arrange-

8.1

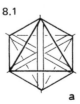

a

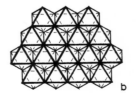

b

ments, to produce more open arrangements of Tensegrity figures.

Four-strut Tensegrity cubes (Diagram 8.2a) can be joined together just like polyhedral cubes (Diagram 8.2b). The lengths of the tendons can be adjusted to vary the shape of the individual units.

Three polyhedral tetrahedra can be joined, vertex to vertex, and stabilized by two large triangles of tendons to form an approximately triangular shape, as shown in Diagram 8.3b. Three four-strut Tensegrity tetrahedra (Diagram 8.3a) can be joined in exactly the same way, as shown in Photograph 27. Three such arrangements of three Tensegrity figures can then be joined together to produce an even larger triangle with a large open space in the middle, as are the polyhedra in Diagram 8.3c.

The lengths of the extra tendons can be adjusted to curve or distort the figure.

Diagram 8.4 shows how 16 polyhedral icosahedra can be joined together, edge to edge, and stabilized by a set of eight triangles of tendons, four on the top and four underneath. There are four gaps between the figures, which could have been filled with further icosahedra. This would have stabilized the assembly, making the extra tendons unnecessary. The tendons of an expanded octahedron (Photograph 1) define all but six of the edges of a slightly distorted icosahedron, so the sixteen polyhedral icosahedra can be replaced by sixteen Tensegrity expanded octahedra and stabilized by the eight triangles of tendons to create the figure shown in Photograph 28. This framework of expanded octahedra, though it looks very delicate, is surprisingly strong.

The Construction of Large Figures in General

The methods of assembly described in the four appendices here are for relatively small models which can be constructed on a table. When building larger figures, factors such as tolerances and weight, which are of little consequence with the smaller models, can be critical. Construction techniques are important, as the loads on the members may be greater during assembly than they are once a figure is completed. Junctions between members

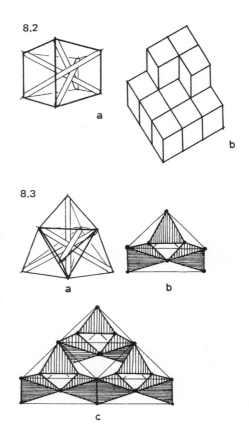

8.2

a

b

8.3

a

b

c

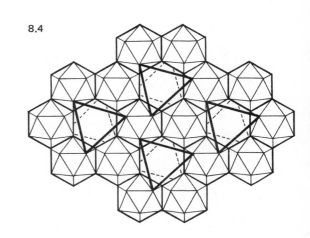

8.4

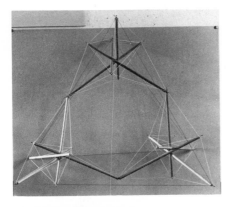

27. Three joined Tensegrity tetrahedra

28. A frame work of expanded octahedra

29. A mast made of six cuboctahedra

must be carefully designed so that they are not sources of weakness. A final concern with larger figures is to allow sufficient working space for the erection of the structure. On the other hand, one advantage of the larger figures is that with them it is easier to use such devices as turnbuckles to permit the adjustment of the sizes of components.

The following examples describe some larger figures and some of the problems one can encounter in building them.

Construction of a Mast of Cuboctahedra

Six polyhedral cuboctahedra can be joined at common square faces to form the mast shown in Diagram 8.5. A slightly taller figure can be made by joining the cuboctahedra at common triangular faces, but this does not result in such an interesting Tensegrity mast. Each polyhedron can be replaced with a circuit-pattern Tensegrity cuboctahedron, to produce the mast shown in Photograph 29. If a model of a circuit-pattern cuboctahedron is placed on one of its square faces, it can be seen that it is enantiomorphic, so care must be taken to build the desired version of the figure each time. In this mast, all the cuboctahedra are alike, though the two different versions can be mixed if desired.

The struts for this structure were 3-foot lengths of dowel, half an inch in diameter. The struts were connected with 3-inch lengths of plastic tubing (garden hose) into which machine screws had been driven and fixed with nuts, as shown in Diagram 8.6a. The heads of the screws projected so that the tendons could be attached to them. Since four struts met at vertices shared by two cuboctahedra, two lengths of tube were fixed to each machine screw to create four-way strut connectors for those vertices, as shown in Diagram 8.6b.

Stainless-steel safety-lock wire, a wire used to prevent nuts from vibrating loose on aircraft, was used for the tendons, as it is easy to bend, is very strong, and does not stretch very much. Piano wire is very difficult to bend, and other types of wire are often too

8.5

8.6

a

b

ductile or else break too easily. Ropes and strings tend to be too elastic for large structures.

The mast was started at one end and components added till the figure was complete. Since the end face of the mast was a square face of a cuboctahedron, the Tensegrity figures were assembled in a slightly different way than the one described in Appendix 3, as is evident in Diagram 8.7. The numbers on the diagram identify the four-way and two-way connectors. The screws on the connectors should always have their heads pointing outwards, since the tendons are on the outside of the figure.

When working with wire, it is wise to wear a pair of gloves to protect one's hands from sharp ends and from the blisters earned by pulling on the wire to straighten it.

The tendons are added by fixing the end of the wire securely to one of the machine screws and then measuring off an appropriate length. It is much quicker to measure the tendons with a stick cut to the desired length than with a ruler or tape, as it saves the time of reading the calibrations. When measuring the tendon, the wire should be reasonably taut and free from kinks. A good way of measuring the lengths is to rest the measuring stick against the machine screw and then pull the wire along it until the wire can be bent over the end of the stick. The bend can be placed around the next machine screw and the wire wound around that screw several times to secure it. The next tendon length can then be measured and fixed as before. Simply winding the wire may not seem a very good way of fixing a tendon, but it is perfectly adequate for the job. It is difficult to tie a wire accurately, and knots can cause weaknesses by kinking the wire.

Tendons should be measured as accurately as possible, as they are not easy to adjust once the figure has been completed. A good way of allowing for inaccuracies is to tie some of the tendons temporarily at first and then replace them once the figure has been completed, the kinks straightened and loose junctions tightened. Those tendons which are common to two cuboctahedra are good ones to tie temporarily at first. Sometimes slack tendons can be shortened by wrapping them round one of the machine screws or by wrapping wire around them and fastening them to other

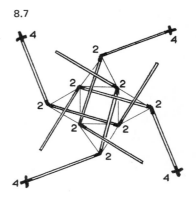

8.7

tendons at that junction. When making such adjustments, it is important to check that the mast is not being pulled out of alignment.

Though these methods for shortening the tendons are crude, they can be effective and neat if done correctly. More sophisticated methods, with such devices as turnbuckles, can be used, but they are expensive and often do not look very tidy.

A Dome Based on the Four-Frequency Icosahedron

The dome shown in Photograph 30 is a circuit-pattern Tensegrity based on a four-frequency icosahedron, truncated just below its equator. The dome is part of the figure shown in Photograph 10, though a few minor alterations have been made to the bottom of the dome, since the complete sphere is not used. The dome is 9 feet, 9 inches in diameter and 6 feet high.

Like the mast described above, this dome was built with half-inch-in-diameter lengths of dowel for struts, lock wire for tendons, and plastic connectors, as described previously. This figure had struts of two lengths, the longer being 36 inches, and three different lengths of tendon. All of the connectors are two-way connectors, except for ten one-way connectors and ten three-way connectors around the base of the figure.

Diagram 8.8 shows a diagrammatic view of the dome from the top. In order to show all of the components in the diagram, a certain amount of distortion has been necessary. The centre of the diagram represents the apex of the dome, and the outer edge represents the base. Two concentric circuits of lines can be traced round the outside of the figure; they represent two circuits of struts, the outer one of which lies directly beneath the inner one. The shorter struts are shown as solid, heavy lines and the longer ones in outline, and it can be seen that the two kinds of strut alternate round the figure, first a long one, then a short one, and so on. To avoid mistakes when assembling the figure, it is worth coding the struts by marking the ends of the shorter ones black and the ends of the longer ones white, then a black end and white

8.8

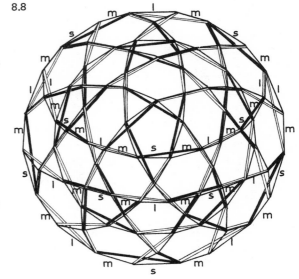

LENGTHS
long tendons (l) ———19·0"
medium tendons(m)–18·0"
short tendons (s) —15·4"

long struts(outlines)–36·0"
short struts(black)— 32·5"
long ½ struts(outlines)–18·5'
short ½ struts(black)—17·5"

30. A dome based on the four-frequency
icosahedron

end will meet at each plastic junction. The truncation of the
sphere causes there to be ten half-struts, of two different lengths,
around the base of the figure. Each half-strut joins with two of the
struts of the base circuit at a three-way plastic connector. The
one-way plastic connectors are used for fixing tendons to the
other strut ends around the base circuit. There are tendons of
three lengths, denoted in the diagram by the letters l (long),
m (medium), and s (short). They follow a sequence of long,
medium, short, medium, long, medium, . . . round the figure, the
short tendons defining the edges of the pentagons and the long
tendons the edges of equilateral triangles.

The figure is built in much the same way as the small model
described in Appendix 3 by forming a pentagon (the apex of the
dome) and adding components systematically till the figure is
complete. It is a good idea to support the structure on chairs
while assembling it, to take some of the strain off individual
components and to save bending over to work. While assembling
the structure, a few struts should be added first and then as
many tendons connected as possible before adding more struts.
Some people are tempted to try to lay out all the struts first,
using the assembly diagram, but they invariably end up with a
confusing jumble of struts, which get in the way when the
tendons are being fixed. As with the mast of cuboctahedra,
construction can be speeded up by using sticks to measure out

the lengths of tendon. The sticks should be clearly marked, as well, to avoid confusion.

Once the figure has been completed, it will be found that its base can be pushed out of shape because the figure is not a complete system, but that can be prevented by fixing the base to the ground or by running cables from the centre of the base to each of the three-way connectors. Any slack tendons can then be tightened, using the techniques described for the mast of cuboctahedra.

A Similar Dome with a Tensile Skin

The struts and tendons in the models of Tensegrity systems represent patterns of forces, and they can be replaced by other components, provided those components can accommodate the forces. It is easy to recognize that the tendon network of the dome just described could be replaced with a plastic skin into which the struts could be slotted, to produce a structure which could be erected very quickly.

The skin for the figure shown in Photograph 31 was made from pieces of polyethylene sheet, each piece representing a hexagonal, pentagonal, or triangular face of the final figure. The individual pieces were heat-sealed to each other with a soldering iron. Since polyethylene stretches very easily, the skin was reinforced by running a nylon thread within a double seam (made with the soldering iron) along each edge of the figure, as shown in Diagram 8.9, and connecting the threads to the nodes which connected the struts to the skin.

The nodes are similar to the ones used for the mast and the dome described earlier, as can be seen in Diagram 8.10. Since wires are not tied to the screws, their heads need not project on the outside. The screws should not project too much on the inside either, as long ends could damage the skin when it is rolled up for storage. The two plastic roofing washers should be screwed tightly together to prevent the screw from tearing the plastic skin.

Once the skin has been completed, the dome can be erected

8.9

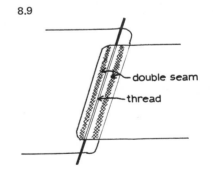

double seam
thread

8.10

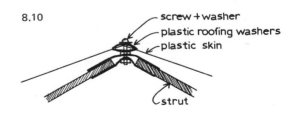

screw + washer
plastic roofing washers
plastic skin
strut

31. A Tensegrity dome with a tensile
skin

very quickly by slotting the struts into the nodes. A larger
version of this dome, approximately 20 feet in diameter, has
been built and erected successfully by the author.

Tensegrity Structures with Pneumatic Struts

The struts of a Tensegrity structure need be neither solid rods nor
substantial tubes but can be delicate lattices, or even inflated
tubes, similar to long balloons. Diagram 8.11 shows a small dome,
approximately 20 feet in diameter and 6 feet high which the
author built in 1969. It was based on the circuit-pattern four-
frequency icosahedron and had struts which were approximately
6 feet long and 8 inches in diameter and was constructed from
polyethylene film. The tendons for the figure were made from
stout sail-maker's twine. Air was supplied to the tubes with a
compressor, which also was used to replace any air which
escaped through accidental small holes in the tubes. Unless the
tubes are built with a very good quality material and with very
high standards of workmanship, they inevitably lose air, so
further air is needed in many cases. The structure would have
been very untidy and complex if air had been supplied
individually to each tube by lengths of small-diameter tube from
the compressor. Luckily, short lengths of tubing could be
used to connect the ends of struts and so allow air to pass from

8.11

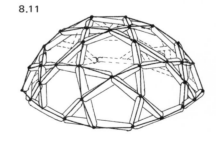

one strut to another. The figure was erected by laying it out and then inflating it slowly until the tubes were sufficiently filled to allow them to be pushed into place.

A Plywood Dome Based on a Tensegrity System

It has been stated that some structures derived from Tensegrity systems do not look very much like the stick-and-string models described earlier. A good example is the plywood dome shown in Photographs 32 and 33, which was derived from the circuit-pattern system based on the six-frequency icosahedron (Photograph 11).

32. A plywood dome based on the six-frequency icosahedron

33. Close-up of the plywood dome shown in Photograph 32

In every circuit-pattern Tensegrity system, each strut is accompanied by two tendons which span from each of its ends to a common node, as in Diagram 8.12a. In this dome each strut and its associated pair of tendons were replaced by a piece of plywood, shaped as in Diagram 8.12b. The top part of each piece is a triangle whose edges are defined by the lengths of the strut and its two associated tendons. The bottom part of each component is a continuation of the top part and serves to strengthen the component. The ends of the bottom part have to be cut at an angle so that each component can be joined to adjacent components. The idea was that each component carried the tensile and compressive forces shown by the Tensegrity system.

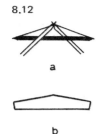

8.12

a

b

Though many materials could have been used, plywood was chosen for the structure because it was relatively inexpensive, lightweight, and, above all, easy to work and shape with simple tools. This dome was 17 feet in diameter and 6 feet high and was made from five 8-foot-by-4-foot sheets of half-inch plywood. The ends of the individual components were bolted to mild steel strips which passed through a slot cut in the components between them.

(The author thanks Doug Money and Bill Lulias for their help in building this structure while they were students in the Department of Design at Southern Illinois University at Carbondale.)

Conclusion

It is impossible to predict the relevance or importance of Tensegrity. The examples discussed in this chapter have primarily been in the field of structure, though it is likely that some of the most important applications of Tensegrity could lie elsewhere. The author hopes that the information in this book will allow readers with many backgrounds to become familiar with these figures. He hopes that they will enjoy building and studying the figures and that many ideas and many applications of Tensegrity will result from their studies.

General Materials and Techniques for Making Models

A proper understanding of Tensegrity can only be gained by building and studying models of the figures. The materials and methods described in these appendices have been tested extensively by the author and his students at the Department of Design, Southern Illinois University at Carbondale. Some readers may find alternatives easier to use, but the author found that most people who tried alternative methods eventually reverted to the ones described here. Though the materials suggested here are relatively inexpensive, careful workmanship will result in very elegant models.

It is best to build a model in two stages. In the first stage a set of rough "working" struts and tendons is assembled, to form a crude model of the figure. In the second stage, the struts and tendons of that model are replaced, one at a time, by better components, to complete the model. Though this may appear time-consuming, it is actually quicker and results in much more accurate models than if the final version were built straight away.

Most of the Tensegrity figures described in this book are based on polyhedra, and it is useful to be able to refer to a model of the appropriate polyhedron when constructing a Tensegrity figure. Readers who are unfamiliar with polyhedra may find it worth studying and building some models of them before attempting the more complex Tensegrity models, so they will be familiar with the three-dimensional symmetries they will encounter.

Struts

One of the best materials for struts is dowel — long, circular wooden rods which can be bought in many hardware stores, hobby shops, and lumberyards. Dowel 3/8 inch in diameter is suitable for most models, but readers may want to experiment with different diameters. Dowel, being a natural material, is never exactly straight, but one should select lengths which are as straight as possible, as bent dowel often has a grain which is not straight and so may split when being worked.

Dowel usually comes in 3-foot lengths, so each length can be cut with a fine-toothed saw to provide 4 struts, each 9 inches long. Twelve-inch struts tend to be longer than necessary and 6-inch struts too short to handle easily.

Fitting Tendons

Small-diameter nails can be driven into the ends of each strut as shown in Diagram A1.1 and the tendons attached to those nails. The best nails to use are 18-gauge wire brads, about 1 inch long, as their small heads look neat and it is easier to loop tendons over them than over nails with larger heads. Steel pins can look a lot neater than brads and are less likely to split the dowel when driven into it, but they bend easily and may even snap. Screw eyes could be used, but it is harder to fix tendons to them and they do not look as neat as brads. They are also comparatively expensive.

If the dowel splits when the brads are driven in, it sometimes helps to blunt the points of the brads before using them. A blunted nail smashes its way through the wood, rather than prising the wood fibres apart and splitting the strut. For the working struts, used in the first, rough models, two nails should be driven into each end of a strut, with a wide gap between them and with their ends protruding at least half an inch, as shown in Diagram A1.2, left. Struts for the finished models need only one pin in each end, and that pin need only protrude a quarter of an inch, as shown at right. A more elegant strut for final models will be described later in this chapter.

Constructing Working Models

The first stage in building a model is to use the working struts with two pins in each end and to use rubber bands as tendons. When

A1.1

A1.2

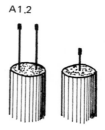

working with rubber bands, one should be VERY CAREFUL, INDEED, as they can slip and propel struts from the model in a potentially dangerous way. At first it is worth using bands which do not pull too strongly, like Number 14 rubber bands (about 2 inches long) and later move on to Number 12 bands (about 1 1/2 inches long). The latter will make much stronger models, but will project struts outwards at higher velocities in the event of a collapse. It is always worth building the smaller models first, to develop the model-making skills, before trying the larger ones.

When building models with rubber bands, it can be seen that if there were only one nail in each end, the bands could slip down the strut, as in Diagram A1.3, left, but that the second nail could prevent this, as at right. A further advantage of having two nails in each end is that bands can be "parked" on the one nail while replacing or removing tendons on the other.

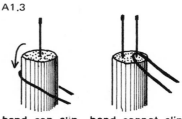

A1.3

band can slip   band cannot slip

Even with two pins in the end of a strut, some rubber bands can slip along a nail, as in Diagram A1.4a, and eventually slip off it. Such tendons should be secured by slipping other bands (tendons) over them to hold them on the nails, as illustrated in Diagram A1.4b. If there is no suitable tendon to do this with, an extra band can be run the whole length of the strut to secure the wandering rubber band, as in Diagram A1.4c.

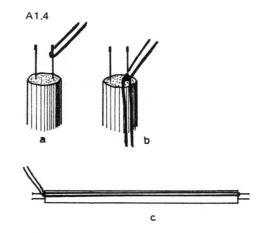

A1.4

a   b

c

A great advantage of a model built with rubber-band tendons is that it can be twisted and deformed to explore what variations in shape can be achieved. Struts and tendons can easily be added or removed, and the model will change its shape accordingly — or collapse, if too many members are removed. In such a way many variations on an original model can be explored very easily. Some final advantages of this type of model is the speed with which it can be built and dismantled and the fact that its components need not be scrapped.

Inevitably, there are disadvantages, the most annoying being the great elasticity of the tendons. This means that the figures sag badly under their own weights, which may prevent many tests and observations being made. The rubber bands also perish in time, especially in hot, dry conditions. Luckily, it is easy to replace the tendons with a less elastic material, as is explained later.

More Permanent Models: Struts

Once a model with rubber-band tendons has been completed, its struts and tendons can be replaced by more permanent, more elegant components. The original, working struts can be retained if desired, but when the new tendons are tied in place, only one pin will be needed in the end of each strut, as the new tendons are less likely to slip.

Very elegant struts can be made from dowel if a certain amount of time and care is taken. Once the dowel has been cut to suitable lengths, a nail should be driven halfway into the ends of each strut. The nail should then be withdrawn, leaving a nail hole in each end. Each strut end can now be pointed, as in Diagram A1.5, by rotating it against a belt sander or a sanding disc. Some people have tried pencil sharpeners, but they usually produce very ragged points. The struts should then be sanded lightly with a fine sandpaper to remove any rough surfaces. The next step is to replace the wire brads in the holes at the ends of each strut. The reason for preforming the holes is that if the nails were driven in at this point for the first time, the dowels would split, because their thickness has been reduced at the ends.

Now the struts can be painted. A good finish can be obtained with two coats of enamel, the first coat priming the wood and the second giving it a smooth, glossy finish. The author prefers bright colours like reds, yellows, blues, black, and white, as he has found that the more discreet colours tend to produce insipid models. The metallic look of struts painted with aluminum paint sounds attractive, but it is hard to get a even finish with that paint, and the struts tend to look gray once dust has settled on them. Since the dowels are wooden, very attractive finishes can be obtained by staining the struts or by varnishing them to emphasize the grain. But, of all the paints and colours, white is one of the most effective, as white models look crisp and tend to photograph better than models with struts of any other colour.

The best and quickest way of painting struts is to use a large, inexpensive watercolour brush or a small (up to a half-inch wide) household paintbrush. Spraying does not coat the struts evenly, and dipping them coats them too heavily. One starts painting by

A1.5

nail hole
pointed end

holding the nail at one end of the strut, letting the other end rest on a piece of newspaper. The strut can be rotated between one's fingers and painted as it turns. The strut can then be held by the nail at the painted end with the unpainted end resting on the newspaper, and the strut rotated to allow the unpainted part to be painted. In such a way the struts can be painted completely without getting very much paint on one's fingers. It is important not to coat the struts too thickly, as the paint will then form blobs and will take a long time to harden. Once the struts are painted, they can be placed with their nails resting on two pieces of scrap lumber to dry, as shown in Diagram A1.6. Using these techniques it is possible to paint sixty struts an hour without too much difficulty. Once the first coat has hardened, the struts should be sanded lightly to remove any rough surfaces and a second coat of paint applied. It is worth waiting a few days to allow the second coat of paint to become really hard before using the struts, to avoid the risk of spoiling the carefully prepared surfaces.

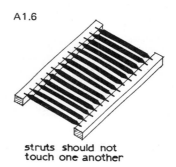

A1.6

struts should not
touch one another

Struts can also be made from materials other than dowel. Many suitable natural materials can be found in the garden or the countryside, such as bamboo or straight twigs or ash or hazel. Such materials, besides costing nothing, have an attractive finish already, so need less work, though it may be worth varnishing them to emphasize the texture of the bark.

Rods and tubes of metal or plastic can be used as struts, though it may not be easy to connect the tendons to them. Small screws can be driven into some rods or holes can be drilled into their ends through which the tendons can be threaded, as in Diagram A1.7, but such junctions are imprecise and do not look very tidy. The easiest way of connecting tendons to a tube is to pack its ends with something to which a nail or other fastening can be secured.

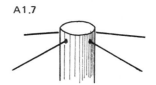

A1.7

Of course, the reader may find other materials and may even decide to use his working struts in the final model. However, the latter may not result in such an attractive model and the shortcut be regretted later.

More Permanent Models: Tendons

The best tendon material the author has found is *braided nylon fishing line*. A line with a breaking strength of 15 pounds is strong enough for most models, and the author has frequently used 7-pound line for lightweight models. Though stronger lines can be found, they are thicker and produce clumsy looking models.

One of the main advantages of a nylon line is that it is slightly elastic, but not overelastic, so it can be tied very tightly to produce highly tensioned models. The slight elasticity helps take up the inevitable inaccuracies; if the tendons were inelastic and one tendon slightly too long, the figure would be slack and look very untidy. *Braided* nylon fishing line is much better than monofilament, as it is more flexible and thus makes knot-tying a lot easier. Monofilament also tends to slip after it has been tied, resulting in annoying inaccuracies and distortions.

Other materials sometimes considered include elastic cords of various types, but they are usually too elastic for most situations. Button thread, carpet thread, and thick cotton at first appear to be strong enough for tendons, but if a model is built from any of them, it will be found that its tendons snap very easily. This is because a knot makes the thread weaker at that point. So it is always worth testing a thread by tying a knot in it and giving it a sharp tug; it is surprising how many apparently strong threads snap easily at the knot.

Wire is sometimes used for tendons, but it is not very elastic and so must be measured very accurately if none of the tendons are to be slack. Another problem with wire is that it does not always return to its original lengths after it has been loaded, so sagging tendons may result. It can be difficult to remove kinks from some wires, and some wires are very easily snapped. Where wire really comes into its own is in larger figures, as is discussed in Chapter 8.

More Permanent Models: Tying the Tendons

When replacing the rubber bands of the working model with fishing line, cut the fishing line as few times as possible. This will save time, as each time the line is cut, its ends must be tied securely to prevent their coming undone. A lot of time can be saved also if the tendons are tied with simple loops formed by thumb knots and half hitches. Though fancier knots can be used, they take longer to tie and are no more effective. The first step is to form a loop at the end of the line and then pull the tendon through the loop, as in Diagram A1.8a, pulling the ends tight to form a knot with a loop protruding from it. One of the tendons coming from this loop is fixed, and the other will run when the loop is made bigger or smaller, as indicated in Diagram A1.8b. It is important that the end which runs is not the short end. The loop is slipped over a nail and pulled tight. This knot will tend to slip, so a half hitch should be added, as in Diagram A1.8c, to make it really secure.

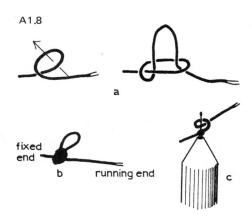

A1.8

a

fixed end

b   running end   c

Once the line has been fastened to the strut, a tendon can be measured and fastened to the next strut. Rather than measure each length with a ruler, it is quicker to cut a measuring stick of an appropriate length from a waste piece of dowel and measure each tendon against it. This saves all the time involved in trying to read the calibrations on a ruler. Pull the tendon along the stick, as shown in Diagram A1.9, and form a loop at the end, as described in the preceding paragraph. With practice, one learns how to slip the knot along the line just prior to tightening it so that it is positioned exactly where it is desired. It is important to have the loop growing or contracting at the expense of the free end of the line, as shown, and not at the expense of the measured length, as this would obviously change its length. The loop can be slipped over the next strut, pulled tight, the length of the tendon checked with the measuring stick, and a half hitch added to stop the knot slipping. The process can be repeated for as many tendons as may be necessary. When a tendon has to be cut, its ends should be secured with a few extra half hitches to make sure it does not undo itself.

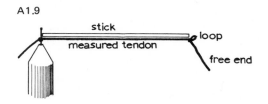

A1.9

stick

measured tendon

loop

free end

There are several points concerning the length of the tendons. The first is that it is important to measure all the tendons when they are pulled tight, and to measure every length at about that same tension. The second point is that as one builds, allowances must be made for the elasticity of tendons; otherwise, a very floppy model will result. Often, especially with larger figures, it may appear that the tendons are much too short and that the saucer-shaped figure being produced cannot possibly become spherical. However, it is important not to try to compensate by tying the rest of the tendons slightly longer. The rest of the tendons should be tied the same length. When the figure is complete, they will all stretch equally to produce a spherical model.

Since so much hinges on the degree of model-making accuracy and on the stretching quality of fishing line, one of the best ways of finding out how long to tie the tendons is by the experience of building models. The experience gained from one model can usually be used on other, related models, even if they are not exactly the same. Tendon lengths can always be estimated by measuring the tendons on the rubber-band model and taking averages, subtracting a bit to allow for the stretch of the tendon. (The tendon lengths given in these appendices are given to the nearest sixteenth of an inch.)

As with the models built from rubber bands, some tendons may slip along the nail, as in Diagram A1.10a, with a risk of ultimately slipping off. Apart from that, such a joint looks very untidy. So it is always worth wrapping the fishing line round any existing tendons at a nail, tying a half hitch to join them, as shown in Diagram A1.10b, before tying the next length of tendon.

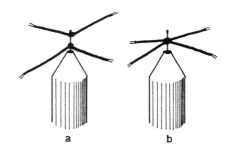

a   b

One final advantage of building models with rubber bands before replacing them with fishing line, instead of tying them with fishing line from scratch, is that the latter method may require a lot of space, particularly for larger models, and one's back gets very tired bending over the struts (which have a tendency to move). With a rubber-band model, the parts are soon brought into the right arrangement, and one can then retire to a comfortable chair in front of the TV to tie the fishing-line tendons.

Recording Work

Since so little information on Tensegrity has been published to date and since it is so tragically easy to forget those valuable first impressions, it is worth making notes on any thoughts and observations that occur while working, especially when building an original figure. A photographic record of the models is particularly valuable, as many of them will eventually be damaged, given away, or cannibalized for other models.

Building Models of Certain Diamond-Pattern Systems

Example — The Twelve-strut Three-layer System (Photograph 3)

The first step is to lay out the 12 struts as shown in Diagram A2.1 and tie all the tendons indicated by unbroken lines in fishing line, using the techniques described in Appendix 1. The tendons indicated in the diagram by broken lines (at the top and the bottom of the sketch) should not be tied at this stage. The 6 tendons shown as unbroken lines with loops in them cannot be tied yet, but should be measured and loops formed at the appropriate points so they can be connected later to X, Y, or P. If the struts move too much when the tendons are being tied, they can be taped to the table temporarily. A figure with struts 9 inches long should have tendons approximately 5 1/16 inches long.

Having checked that all the tendons are tied correctly, the strut and tendon ends indicated by the letters A, B, C, D, P, Q, R, S, X, and Y should be labelled according to the diagram. This can be done with small pieces of tape or gummed paper, but the main point is to label everything clearly, to avoid confusion during later stages. Next, a strip of paper should be placed over the central part of the assembly to prevent the struts and tendons from tangling, and then the left- and right-hand sides of the assembly can be brought over, as shown in Diagram A2.2, to allow the 6 unconnected tendons to be connected to X, Y, or P, as appropriate.

The final tendons to add are those indicated by broken lines in Diagram A2.1, to complete the top square ($ABCD$) and the bottom square ($PQRS$) of tendons. Unlike the other tendons, these should be rubber bands instead of fishing line. At this point the model is almost complete, and it should be checked to ensure

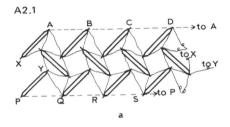

A2.1

a

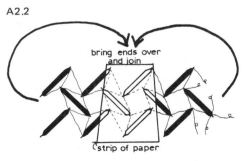

A2.2

bring ends over and join

strip of paper

b

that the tendons define diamond shapes about each strut and that there are 4 tendons joined to each strut end. Any tendons which are too long or too short should be adjusted. The rubber bands can then be replaced by fishing line, using the average length of the rubber bands as a guide and allowing for the elasticity of the fishing line. In theory, each of these tendons should be 5 1/16 inches long, but the accumulated inaccuracies of the previously tied tendons may necessitate a slightly different length.

Any of the other diamond pattern figures described in Chapter 3 can be built by this method if the appropriate numbers of struts are laid out and connected in the way just described. The larger figures will need slightly shorter tendons than were used in this example.

Building Models of
Circuit-Pattern Figures

Models of the circuit-pattern figures described in Chapter 4 and
Chapter 5 can be built relatively quickly by the following method.
It is a good idea to start by building some of the smaller examples
in order to master the general techniques, before attempting the
larger figures. At first the general approach will be described,
using the *cuboctahedron* (Photograph 4) as an example; then
instructions for the other figures discussed in Chapter 4 and
Chapter 5 will be outlined.

Each model is first built from struts with two nails in each end,
using rubber bands as tendons. Once the model is completed, its
struts and tendons can be replaced by more elegant components,
as described in Appendix 1.

The first step is to prepare the appropriate number of struts by
linking rubber bands in pairs and pulling them tight as in Diagram
A3.1a, and then looping a pair over each strut, as in Diagram
A3.1b. The bands should only be slipped over one of the nails in
each strut end; otherwise they could slip down the strut. Each
rubber band will form one of the tendons on the Tensegrity model.

The next step is to become familiar with the tendon network
and try to visualize how the strut circuits interweave within it, by
studying a drawing or a model of the appropriate polyhedron. A
model is preferable to a drawing, as it is three-dimensional, like the
Tensegrity system, which makes it easier to work out the arrangement of struts and tendons. The Tensegrity cuboctahedron

A3.1

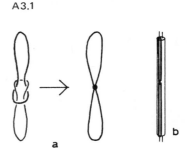

A3.2

12 struts form 4 triangles.
24 tendons ($5\frac{3}{16}$" long for 9" struts).

(Photograph 4) is based on the polyhedron shown in Diagram
A3.2. It has 12 struts and 24 tendons, as noted, and its tendons
are 5 3/16 inches long if its struts are 9 inches long.

Every circuit-pattern model can be built by joining a few struts
together so that their tendons define one of the faces of the
polyhedron and then adding further struts systematically till the
model is complete. So, the first step in building a model of the
Tensegrity cuboctahedron is to join 3 struts so that an end of each
is connected to the knot between the pair of rubber bands on
another strut, to define a triangle of struts, as shown in Diagram
A3.3a. It is important to make sure that the rubber bands cannot
slip, by looping each band of a linked pair over separate nails and
securing them with a third rubber band, as shown in Diagram
A3.3b.

The next step is to connect 6 more struts to the original 3 struts
as in Diagram A3.4, using the same techniques for connecting
them as before. Then, having made sure that all the tendons are on
the topside (the eventual outside) of the struts, connect 3 pairs of
strut ends by pushing them together and wrapping the adjacent
tendons round the nails, to define 3 more triangular faces of the
cuboctahedron. All joints should be made on the topside of the
assembly.

Then join the strut ends as indicated by the arrows in the left
sketch of Diagram A3.5, to form the first triangle of struts. At the
same time 3 of the square faces of the cuboctahedron will be
defined by the tendons, and the figure will take on a three-
dimensional form, approximately as shown in the right-hand
sketch of Diagram A3.5, though there will be a certain amount of
distortion because the rubber bands are unlikely to have stretched
evenly. It is well worth checking that all the struts are on the inside
and all the tendons and joints between the struts are on the
outside of the assembly.

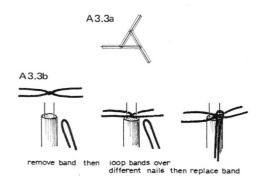

A3.3a

A3.3b

remove band   then   loop bands over
different nails then replace band

A3.4

A3.5

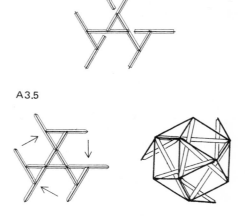

The figure can now be turned over and the last 3 struts added (to span between *A-A*, *B-B*, and *C-C*, as shown in Diagram A3.6) to complete the last 3 triangles of struts. At the same time the last 3 pairs of rubber bands can be connected, to complete the network of tendons.

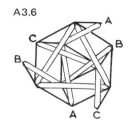

A3.6

Before the figure is really complete there are three checks to make. The first is to see that the tendons really do define the edges of a cuboctahedron. The second point to check is that no strut is pressing hard against another somewhere in midspan. This is usually caused by one strut's passing on the wrong side of another. It can be rectified by disconnecting one of them and replacing it correctly. One of the great advantages of rubber-band models is the ease with which such adjustments can be made. The final check is to make sure that all the struts are on the inside of the figure and all the tendons on the outside.

Once the model with rubber-band tendons is completed, those tendons and struts can be replaced by more permanent tendons and more elegant struts, as described in Appendix 1. This is worth doing, as a rubber-band version of the model will tend to be untidy and distorted, compared with one that has fishing-line tendons. The tendons for a figure with struts 9 inches long will be approximately 5 3/16 inches long, though allowances must be made for the elasticity of the tendons.

Other circuit-pattern figures can be built by similar techniques, following the assembly sequences shown later in this appendix. Sometimes the weight of the struts causes a model to sag, but when the rubber bands are replaced by less elastic tendons, the model will not sag as badly, especially when those tendons are tied tightly and accurately. When assembling these models, problems can be avoided if the following precautions and rules are observed:

1. Do not attempt to do too many steps at the same time, but add a few struts systematically and make as many connections as possible before adding further struts.

2. Check frequently for mistakes. Check that the strut circuits interweave, passing under one, over the next, and so on. Check that the struts are on the inside and that all the tendons and junctions are on the outside. Check that the circuits of struts

follow circuits of tendons around the figure and that those tendons define the edges of the appropriate polyhedron.

3. Count out the correct number of struts before starting, and when building a large model, divide them into small groups so that a quick check can be made on the number of struts already built into the figure at any time. This is a useful way of determining whether a particular step really has been completed.

4. Connect strut ends whenever possible, to reduce the chances of confusion. Connect tendons securely, and always reconnect any parts which have become undone as soon as possible, to reduce the chances of the figure's undoing itself.

5. Use a model of an appropriate polyhedron as a guide, and do not hesitate to label strut ends or rubber bands, to reduce the chances of errors.

Once the model with rubber-band tendons has been completed, it should be checked for mistakes, as mentioned for the cuboctahedron. More elegant struts and less elastic tendons can then be substituted for the existing struts and rubber bands, making appropriate allowances for the elasticity of the new tendon material. Some figures will have struts and tendons of more than one length but, provided those differences are not too great, the rubber-band model can be built with struts of the same length and the rubber bands will take up the inaccuracies. When the more elegant components are substituted, they should be of the appropriate lengths.

In the following sets of assembly sequences it has been assumed that the reader will begin with the tendons on top of the struts, simply because it is easier to work that way. At a certain point, which is indicated in each example, it is easier to turn the model over before continuing. Sometimes the reader's assemblies may not look exactly like the diagrams. Sometimes this will be because of the difficulties of showing a three-dimensional arrangement on a two-dimensional page and sometimes it will be because the rubber bands in the model are stretching unevenly.

A3.7

30 struts form 6 pentagons
90 tendons (4 $\frac{12}{16}$" long for 9" struts)

The Icosidodecahedron (Photograph 7)

A3.8

Join 5 struts to form a pentagon of tendons.

A3.9

Add 5 struts, and connect the strut ends to form 5 triangles of tendons.

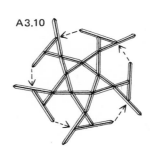

A3.10

Add 10 more struts, and connect 5 pairs of ends to form 5 more triangles of tendons. Then join the 5 pairs of strut ends as indicated by the arrows. This will form 5 more pentagons of tendons and the first pentagonal circuit of struts.

The figure will now be becoming three-dimensional, and it can be turned over.

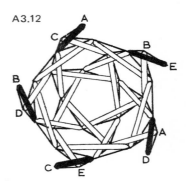

A3.11

A3.12

Add 5 more struts (shown solid), and define 5 more triangles of tendons. Finally, add the last 5 struts to span between *A-A*, *B-B*, *C-C*, *D-D*, and *E-E*, to complete the rest of the pentagonal circuits of struts, and connect the tendons to define the rest of the edges of the icosidodecahedron.

A3.13
24 struts form 6 squares
48 tendons (4$\frac{14}{16}$" long for 9" struts)

The Small Rhombicuboctahedron and the Snub Cube (Photograph 8)

Whichever of these figures is to be constructed, it is easier to ignore any distortions and build it as if the tendons defined the edges of an undistorted small rhombicuboctahedron. Once the rubber-band model has been completed, extra tendons can be added, either to prevent the 12 square faces from distorting, or to define all the edges of a snub cube. The 6 squares of tendons which do not distort are the ones which can be lined up with the faces of a cube.

Join 4 struts to form a square of tendons.

A3.14

Add 4 pairs of struts and connect the strut ends to form 4 more squares of tendons (these squares will distort later).

A3.15

A3.16

Add 4 more pairs of struts, and connect the strut ends to form 4 more squares of tendons (these squares do not distort).

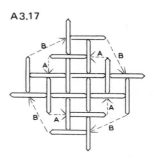

A3.17

Turn the assembly over, and join the 4 pairs of strut ends, as indicated by the arrows marked 'A'. This will form the first square circuit of struts and 4 triangles of tendons. Then join the 4 pairs of strut ends, as indicated by the arrows marked B. This will form a second square circuit of struts parallel to the plane of the first circuit of struts and will also form 4 more squares of tendons.

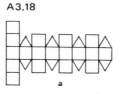

A3.18

The final step is to add the last 4 struts, to complete the other 4 square circuits of struts, and to connect the tendons to define the rest of the edges of a distorted small rhombicuboctahedron. When connecting the last few tendons, care must be taken not to define the edges of a figure called the pseudo-rhombicuobocta-hedron. The net diagrams show that the pseudo-rhombicuobocta-hedron (b) is like a small rhombicuboctahedron (a) with its top part rotated through 45°. Fortunately, it is fairly simple to correct such a mistake on a model that has rubber bands as tendons.

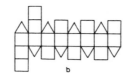

A3.19

If the tendons are to define all the edges of a snub cube, an extra tendon should be added across the shorter diagonal of each distorted square of tendons, as shown.

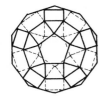

A3.20
60 struts form 12 pentagons
120 tendons ($4\frac{10}{16}$" long for 9" struts)

The Small Rhombicosidodecahedron
and the Snub Dodecahedron (Photograph 9)

Whichever of these two figures is to be constructed, it is easier to build it by ignoring the distortions of the squares of tendons and to pretend that the tendons are to define the edges of a small rhombicosidodecahedron. Once the model has been completed, an extra tendon can be added to each square face, either to prevent the small rhombicosidodecahedron from distorting or to define the rest of the edges of a snub dodecahedron.

A3.21

Join 5 struts, to form a pentagon of tendons.

A3.22

Add 10 struts, and connect their ends, to form 5 squares of tendons. Then join the 5 pairs of strut ends as indicated by the arrows so that 5 triangles of tendons are formed, as well as the first pentagonal circuit of struts.

A3.23

Turn the assembly over.

Add 5 pairs of struts, connecting their ends so that 5 more squares of tendons are defined.

Add 5 more struts (shown solid), and connect the 5 pairs of ends as indicated by the arrows. This will form 5 more pentagons of tendons.

By this point, enough of the figure will have been assembled to make it fairly easy to work out how to add the rest of the components. Any problems which may be encountered can usually be resolved by studying a model of the polyhedron. Since this figure has so many struts, their weight will cause a model with rubber-band tendons to sag very badly. If the rubber bands are replaced with less elastic tendons, the new tendons should be tied very tightly to prevent the model from sagging.

A3.26

15 struts form a continuous circuit

30 tendons ($5\frac{2}{16}''$ long for $9''$ struts)

The Fifteen-Strut Three-Layer Circuit-Pattern System (Photograph 5)

Join 5 struts, to form one of the end pentagons of tendons.

A3.27

Add 5 more struts, and connect their ends to form 5 triangles of tendons.

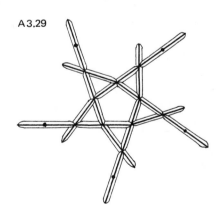

A3.28

Connect the last 5 struts to the ends of the existing struts.

A3.29

Turn the model over, and then join pairs of strut ends as indicated by the arrows to complete the strut circuit and to allow the tendons to define the rest of the edges of the polyhedron. It may be worth labelling the strut ends before joining them, to reduce the chances of joining them incorrectly. The numbers on the diagram indicate the places where the triangles (3) and quadrilaterals (4) of tendons are formed.

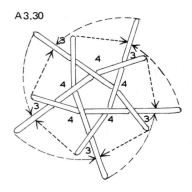

A3.30

A 3.31
20 struts form 5 squares
40 tendons (5" long for 9" struts)

The Twenty-Strut Four-Layer
Circuit-Pattern System (Photograph 6)

Join 5 struts to form one of the end pentagons of tendons.

A 3.32

Add 5 more struts, and connect their ends to form 5 triangles of tendons.

A 3.33

Add 5 more struts; then connect their ends, as indicated by the arrows to form 5 quadrilaterals of tendons.

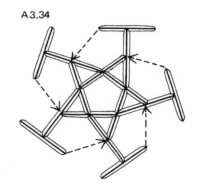

A 3.34

Turn the assembly over. The final 5 struts can then be added (connecting *A-A*, *B-B*, *C-C*, *D-D*, *E-E*) to form the square circuits of struts, and the tendons can be connected to define the rest of the edges of the polyhedron.

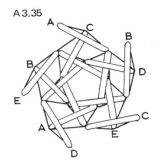

A 3.35

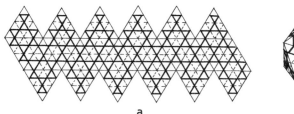

A3.36
120 struts
240 tendons

a   b

The Four-Frequency Icosahedron (Photograph 10)

The geometric basis of this system is more complex than those of
the previous systems, and some form of polyhedral model is
almost essential as a guide for the assembly of the Tensegrity
model. It would take a long time to build a cardboard model of a
four-frequency icosahedron, but a useful guide can be made from a
regular icosahedron. The first sketch shows the net diagram of an
icosahedron, on which the circuits followed by the struts and
tendons are indicated by heavy lines. The second sketch shows the
model produced by cutting out such a net diagram and joining its
edges, to create an icosahedron. The paths of 12 decagonal circuits
of struts can be traced on such a model, as can the network of
tendons (which defines 12 pentagons, 30 hexagons, and 80 triangles on the surface of the figure).

A3.37

Join 5 struts, to form one of the pentagons of tendons.

A3.38

   Add 5 struts and connect their ends to existing struts to define
5 triangles of tendons.

Add 5 pairs of struts and connect the appropriate strut ends, to form 5 more triangles of tendons.

A 3.39

Add 5 more struts and connect the appropriate strut ends, to define 5 hexagons of tendons.

A 3.40

Add 10 more struts, to define 10 more triangles of tendons.

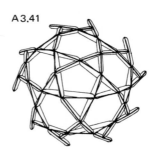

A 3.41

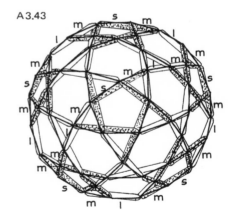

A3.42

Now turn the figure over and add 10 pairs of struts (shown solid) to form 10 more triangles of tendons. Then join 10 pairs of strut ends, as indicated by the arrows, to create the first of the 12 decagonal circuits of struts. Connecting those strut ends will also form 5 more pentagons and 5 more hexagons of tendons.

From this point it is fairly easy to work out how to add the remaining struts and tendons, using the cardboard model and the existing part of the model as guides. The weight of the struts will cause a model of this figure to sag very badly if it has rubber-band tendons, so it is worth replacing the rubber bands with less elastic tendons, which should be tied as tightly as possible.

A3.43

There are several versions of the final figure, one of which has all its struts the same length and all its tendons slightly over half that length, but its strut circuits undulate in an untidy way round the figure. A more elegant version, where the tendons and struts flow more smoothly round the figure, has struts of two different lengths and tendons of three different lengths. There are 60 struts of each length, and if the longer ones are 9 inches long, the shorter ones are 8 2/16 inches long. The two kinds of struts alternate round the figure, first a long one, then a short one, then a long one, and so on. The shorter struts (shaded in the diagram) are associated with tendons which define the pentagons in the tendon network. The longest tendons are 4 12/16 inches long, the medium-length tendons are 4 8/16 inches long, and the shortest are 3 14/16 inches long. The tendons follow the sequence long-medium-short-medium-long-medium (*l-m-s-m-l-m*), and so on round the figure, as shown, with the short lengths defining the edges of the pentagons in the tendon network.

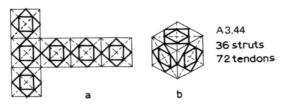

A3.44
36 struts
72 tendons

a   b

The Two-Frequency Cube (Photograph 12)

As with the previous system, it is worth building a simple cardboard model on which the circuits have been sketched, to serve as
a guide when building this Tensegrity system. Sketch *a* shows a net
diagram for a cube, on which the tendon network is sketched in a
heavy line. This diagram can be drawn, cut out, folded, and its
edges joined to form a model of a cube, as shown in sketch *b*.
From this model it can be seen that the tendons define 24 triangles, 6 squares, and 8 hexagons and that the struts form 6
undulating hexagonal circuits within that tendon network.

Join 4 struts, to form one of the squares of tendons.

A3.45

Add 4 struts and connect their ends to form 4 triangles of
tendons.

A3.46

Add 4 pairs of struts to form 4 more triangles of tendons.

A3.47

Add 4 more pairs of struts, to form 4 more triangles of tendons. Then connect the 4 pairs of strut ends, as indicated by the arrows, to define 4 of the hexagons of tendons.

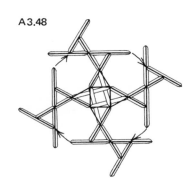

A3.48

Now turn the assembly over, and add the last 12 struts, using the cardboard model as a guide, to complete the figure. This figure usually has struts of two different lengths and tendons of two different lengths. The 24 longer struts are those which span across each face of the cube (shaded in sketch *a*). If those struts are 9 inches long, the 12 shorter ones are 8 14/16 inches long. The longer tendons (*x* on sketch *b*) are 4 12/16 inches long, and the shorter ones (*y*) are 4 10/16 inches long.

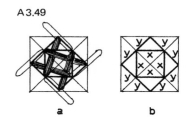

A3.49

a   b

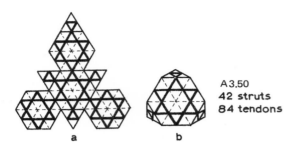

A3.50
42 struts
84 tendons

The Two-Frequency Truncated Tetrahedron (Photograph 13)

As with the two previous examples, it is worth building a simple
cardboard model to serve as a guide when building this Tensegrity
model. Sketch *a* shows a net diagram for a truncated tetrahedron
on which the circuits of tendons appear in heavy lines. From the
model (sketch *b*) it will be seen that the network of tendons
defines 4 hexagons, 12 pentagons, and 28 triangles and that the
struts form 7 hexagonal circuits.

A3.51

Join 6 struts to form one of the hexagons of tendons.

A3.52

Add 6 struts and join the appropriate strut ends, to form
6 triangles of tendons.

A3.53

Add 6 pairs of struts and join the appropriate ends, to form
6 more triangles of tendons. Then join the 6 pairs of strut ends as
indicated by the arrows. This creates 6 pentagons of tendons and
the first hexagonal circuit of struts.

Turn the model over, and add 6 struts (shown solid) to form 6 more triangles of tendons.

A3.54

Add 3 pairs of struts (shown solid) to form 3 more triangles of tendons. Then join the 3 pairs of strut ends as indicated by the arrows, and define 3 pentagons of tendons. In the diagram 5s indicate these pentagons and 6s indicate the positions of the hexagons which will be formed later. Only 6 struts remain to be added, and it should be relatively easy to work out from the cardboard model how to add them.

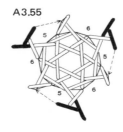

A3.55

One version of this figure has struts of three different lengths if the 24 longest ones (shown solid) in the sketch, are 9 inches long, the 12 shaded struts are 7 12/16 inches long and the other six, shown in outline, will be 7 10/16 inches long. The figure has tendons of three different lengths. Those marked x are 5 6/16 inches long, those marked y are 3 15/16 inches long, and those marked z are 4 inches long.

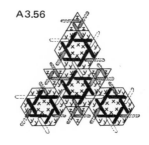

A3.56

Building Models of Zigzag-Pattern Figures

Models of any of the zigzag-pattern figures, even the large ones based on geodesic polyhedra, can be built relatively quickly by the following method. It is worth building some of the simpler, smaller models first, to learn the general techniques, before attempting the more complex ones. First this text describes the general approach, using the *truncated tetrahedron* (Photograph 14) as an example; then it gives instructions for building the other figures described in Chapter 6.

Each model is first built from struts with two nails in each end and rubber bands as tendons. Once the model has been completed, its struts and tendons can be replaced by more elegant components, as described in Appendix 1.

The first step is to prepare the appropriate number of struts by linking rubber bands in threes and attaching a set of them to each strut, as shown in Diagram A4.1a,b. Note that the bands should be looped over one nail at each end; if they were looped over both nails, they could slip down the strut. Each set of bands forms a zigzag of tendons on the final figure, as shown in Diagram A4.1c.

The next step is to become familiar with the tendon network and to visualize how the struts are arranged within that tendon network by studying a drawing or a model of the appropriate polyhedron. A model is better than a drawing, as it is three-dimensional, like the Tensegrity system, which makes it easier to spot the relationships between the struts and the tendons. This Tensegrity system is based on a polyhedron called the truncated tetrahedron, which is shown in Diagram A4.2. It has 6 struts and 18 tendons, as noted, and its tendons are 4 1/16 inches long if its struts are 9 inches long.

A4.1

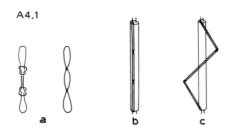

a   b   c

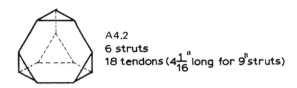

A4.2
6 struts
18 tendons ($4\frac{1}{16}$" long for 9" struts)

The general way of building zigzag-pattern figures is to join a few struts together so that their rubber bands define one of the faces of the polyhedron and then add further struts systematically, to define further faces, until the figure is complete. It is important to make sure that the rubber bands cannot slip and thus allow the figure to disintegrate, by looping each band at a link over different nails and securing them with the third band, as shown in Diagram A4.3.

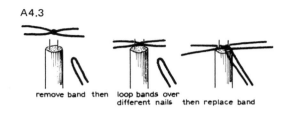

A4.3

remove band then | loop bands over different nails | then replace band

The first part in the assembly of the figure is to take 3 struts and connect one end of each to the tendons of another. The struts will form a triangular arrangement, and 6 tendons will form a large triangular circuit, as shown in Diagram A4.4.

Next, add the other 3 struts, connecting an end of each to one of the vacant knots of the triangular circuit of tendons, to make the triangle into a hexagon, and connecting the ends of existing struts to the tendons of the new struts. This will define 3 triangles of tendons (Diagram A4.5).

Having checked that all the tendons are on top of the struts, turn the assembly over and complete it by connecting the 3 strut ends to the 3 remaining vacant knots, as indicated by the arrows in Diagram A4.6. This will allow the last 3 hexagons and the last triangle of tendons to be defined, and the figure will be complete. It is surprisingly easy to connect the last 3 struts incorrectly, so the reader is strongly advised to label the strut ends and the knots in the rubber bands before attempting to join them.

Once complete, check the model to ensure that the tendons define the edges of a truncated tetrahedron and that none is twisted behind a strut. The struts should also be checked to ensure that none is a diagonal to a hexagonal face, as in Diagram A4.7a, but that each joins vertices belonging to different sets of faces, as in Diagram A4.7b. The latter error is caused by connecting the last 3 strut ends incorrectly, hence the advisability of labelling

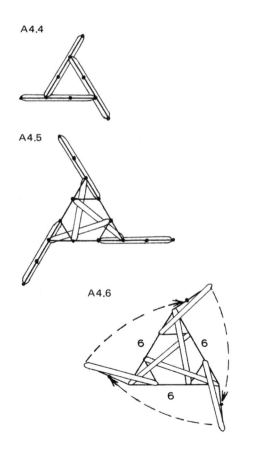

A4.4

A4.5

A4.6

the ends before joining them. The struts and rubber bands can then be replaced by more elegant struts and less elastic tendons, as described in Appendix 1. If the model has 9-inch struts, its tendons should be 4 1/16 inches long, though allowances must be made for the elasticity of the tendon material.

Other zigzag-pattern figures can be built similarly, following the assembly sequences described in the rest of this appendix. Sometimes the weight of its struts will cause a model to sag, but when rubber bands are replaced with less elastic tendons, the model will not sag so badly, especially if its tendons are tied tightly. When assembling the rubber-band models, one can avoid problems by observing the following rules and precautions:

1. Do not attempt too many steps at the same time, but add a few struts systematically and then make as many connections as possible before adding further struts. Make sure the struts are connected to the right knots, using labels where necessary.

2. Count out the correct number of struts before starting, and, when building a large model, divide them into small groups so a quick check can be made on how many struts have been built into the figure at a given time. This is a useful way of checking whether a particular step really has been completed.

3. Make frequent checks for mistakes. Make sure that all the tendons are on the outside and that they define the right network of tendons. Make sure that each strut joins vertices belonging to different faces and does not form a diagonal to a face — especially hexagonal, octagonal, and decagonal faces as shown in Diagrams A4.7 and A4.8.

4. Make connections as soon as possible, to avoid confusion. Always connect the tendons securely and connect any which have become undone as soon as possible, to reduce the chances of the model's disintegrating.

5. Consult a model or drawing of the appropriate polyhedron whenever in doubt about the next step.

Once the model with rubber-band tendons has been completed and given a final check, the more elegant struts and less elastic tendons described in Appendix 1 can be substituted. Allowances must still be made for the elasticity of the new tendon material, as

A4.7

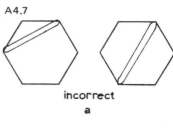

incorrect

a

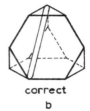

correct

b

A4.8

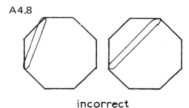

incorrect

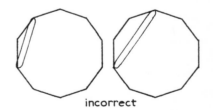

incorrect

it will usually stretch, though not as noticeably as the rubber bands. Some figures will have struts and tendons of more than one length but, provided the differences in those lengths are not too great, the rubber-band model can be built with struts all the same length, as the rubber bands will take up the inaccuracies. When the more elegant components are substituted, however, they should be of the correct lengths.

In the following assembly sequences it is assumed that the reader will begin with the tendons on top of the struts, as it is easier to work that way. At a certain point, which is indicated in each case, it is easier to turn the model over before continuing. Sometimes the reader's assemblies may not look exactly like the diagrams. Sometimes this will be because of the difficulties of showing a three-dimensional arrangement on a two-dimensional page, and sometimes it will be caused by the rubber bands' stretching unevenly. In some of the diagrams appropriate numerals indicate the positions of polygons of tendons, as 6s indicated the positions of hexagons in Diagram A4.6.

A4.9

12 struts

36 tendons ($3\frac{9}{16}$" long for 9" struts)

The Truncated Octahedron and the
Snub Cube (Photograph 15)

Whichever of these figures is to be constructed, it is easier to
ignore the distortions of the hexagonal faces and build it as if the
tendons defined the edges of an undistorted truncated octahedron.
Once this figure has been completed, extra tendons can be added
to define the rest of the edges of the snub cube, if desired.

A4.10

    Join 4 struts so that 4 of their tendons form a small square, one
of the faces of the truncated octahedron.

A4.11

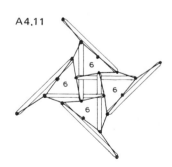

    Add 4 more struts, and connect the strut ends to tendons to
form 4 hexagonal circuits of tendons.

Add the last 4 struts, and connect them so that 4 more squares of tendons are formed.

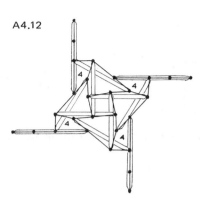

A4.12

Turn the assembly over, and then connect the strut ends, as indicated by the arrows, to form the last 4 hexagons and the last square of tendons.

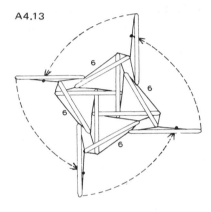

A4.13

The basic figure is complete. If desired, the rest of the edges of a snub cube can be defined by adding 3 tendons of each hexagon, as shown.

A4.14

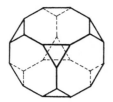

A4.15
12 struts
36 tendons ($3\frac{6}{16}$" long for 9" struts)

The Truncated Cube (Photograph 16)

A4.16

Join 4 struts so that 8 of their tendons form a large square circuit. This will become one of the octagonal faces of the truncated cube.

A4.17

Add 4 struts, and connect them, to form 4 triangles of tendons.

A4.18

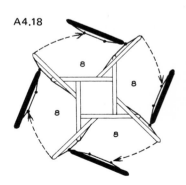

Turn the assembly over, and add the final 4 struts (shown solid). Then connect the 4 strut ends as indicated by the arrows, to form 4 more octagons of tendons. Since it is possible to join them incorrectly, it is worth labelling the strut ends and the knots in the rubber bands before joining them. If this step is performed correctly, it should be obvious how to connect the remaining 4 strut ends, to complete the figure.

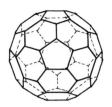

A4.19
30 struts
90 tendons ($3\frac{4}{16}''$ long for 9′ struts)

The Truncated Icosahedron (Photograph 17)

Join 5 struts so that 5 of their tendons define a small pentagon, one of the faces of the truncated icosahedron.

A4.20

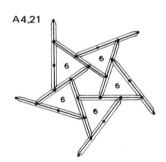

Add 5 struts, and connect them, to form 5 hexagonal circuits of tendons, as shown by 6s in the diagram.

A4.21

Add 5 pairs of struts to form 5 more pentagons of tendons.

A4.22

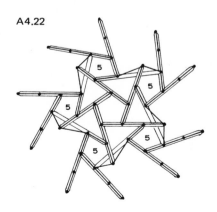

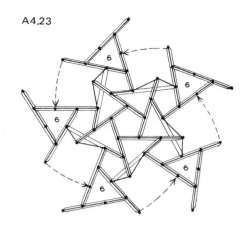

A4.23

Add 5 more struts, so that their tendons allow 5 more hexagons of tendons to be formed. Then connect the 5 strut ends as indicated by the arrows to define 5 more hexagons of tendons.

At this point it is worth turning the model over if this has not been done already. It should be fairly simple to work out how the last 5 struts should be added, to complete the figure. If a *snub dodecahedron* is required, 3 more tendons should be added to each distorted hexagon of tendons, as shown.

A4.24

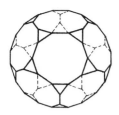

A4.25
30 struts
90 tendons ($3\frac{3}{16}$″ long for 9″ struts)

The Truncated Dodecahedron (Photograph 18)

Join 5 struts so that 10 of their tendons define the edges of a large pentagon. This circuit of tendons will become a decagonal face on the truncated dodecahedron.

A4.26

A4.27

Add 5 struts, and connect them to form 5 triangles of tendons.

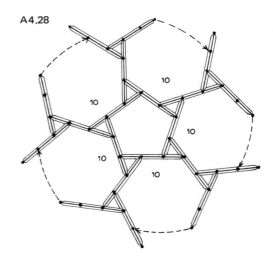

A4.28

Add 5 pairs of struts, to define 5 more triangles of tendons. Then connect the 5 strut ends, as indicated by the arrows, to form 5 more decagonal circuits of tendons.

The assembly should then be turned over, and it should be fairly obvious how the remaining components should be added.

A4.29
24 struts
72 tendons ($3\frac{4}{16}$" long for 9" struts)

The Great Rhombicuboctahedron (Photograph 19)

A4.30

Join 4 struts so that 8 of their tendons define the edges of a large square. This circuit of tendons will become one of the octagonal faces of the great rhombicuboctahedron.

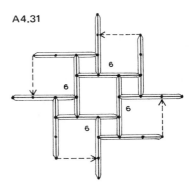

A4.31

Add 4 pairs of struts, to form 4 small squares of tendons. Then connect the 4 strut ends, as indicated by the arrows, to create 4 hexagons of tendons.

The figure can then be turned over and 8 more struts (shown solid) added, to form 4 more small squares of tendons. Then connect 4 strut ends, as shown by the arrows, to define 4 more octagonal circuits of tendons. It should be fairly obvious how to add the last 4 struts to complete the figure.

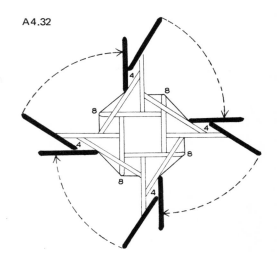

A4.32

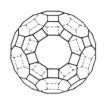

A4.33
60 struts
180 tendons ($3\frac{2}{16}''$ long for $9''$ struts)

The Great Rhombicosidodecahedron (Photograph 20)

Join 5 struts so that 10 of their tendons define the edges of a large pentagon. This circuit of tendons will become one of the decagonal faces of the great rhombicosidodecahedron.

A4.34

Add 5 pairs of struts, and join them so that 5 small squares of tendons are defined. Then connect the strut ends to the tendons, as indicated by the arrows to form 5 hexagons of tendons.

A4.35

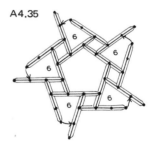

The figure can then be turned over and 5 pairs of struts (shown solid) added, to allow 5 more squares of tendons to be defined. From this point it should be fairly easy to work out how to add the rest of the struts by referring to the part already built or to a model of the polyhedron. Since this model has so many struts, its tendons must be tied very tightly if it is not to sag with its own weight.

A4.36

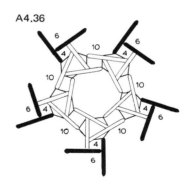

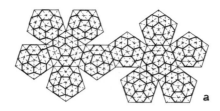

A4.37
90 struts
270 tendons

a   b

The Three-Frequency Dodecahedron (Photograph 21)

The geometric basis of this figure is more complex than those of the previous systems, so some form of polyhedral model is almost essential as a guide. It takes a long time to build an accurate model of a three-frequency dodecahedron, but, fortunately, a useful guide can be made by sketching the struts and tendons of the Tensegrity model on a model of a regular dodecahedron. Sketch *a* shows the net diagram for a dodecahedron with each face subdivided to three frequencies, and the tendon network superimposed with a heavier line. If such a diagram is cut out and then its edges creased and joined, a dodecahedron will result. The struts can be sketched on this model as shown in sketch *b*. From this model it will be seen that the figure will have 90 struts and that its 270 tendons will define 20 undistorted hexagons, 60 distorted hexagons, and 12 pentagons.

Join 5 struts so that 5 of their tendons define the edges of a small pentagon.

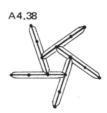

A4.38

Add 5 struts, to form a distorted hexagon of tendons against each edge of the pentagon.

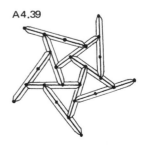

A4.39

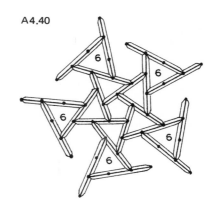

A4.40

Add 5 pairs of struts so that 5 more distorted hexagons of tendons are formed.

A4.41

Add 5 struts (shown solid), to form 5 of the undistorted hexagons of tendons.

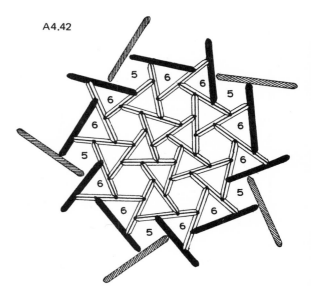

A4.42

Add 10 struts (shown solid) to form 10 more distorted hexagons of tendons. Then add 5 more struts (shown shaded), to form 5 more pentagons of tendons.

The assembly can then be turned over and the rest of the components added, using the cardboard model and existing parts of the assembly as guides. Since this figure has so many struts, the model with rubber-band tendons will sag very badly from its own weight, and, when the rubber bands are replaced, the less elastic tendons must be tied very tightly if the final model is not to sag. One version of this figure has all the struts the same length and all of its tendons a fraction more than one-third that length.

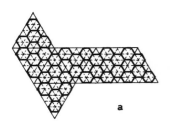

A4.43
48 struts
144 tendons

a   b

The Six-Frequency Octahedron (Photograph 22)

As with the previous system, a simple cardboard model on which
the tendons and struts are sketched will be a useful reference when
building this Tensegrity model. Sketch *a* shows the net diagram of
an octahedron on which the network of tendons for the six-
frequency octahedron has been sketched in heavy lines. Sketch *b*
shows the model of the octahedron produced from such a diagram,
with the strut arrangement sketched upon it. From this model it
can be seen that the Tensegrity system will have 48 struts and
144 tendons, the tendons defining 6 squares, 32 distorted hexagons, and 12 undistorted hexagons.

Join 4 struts so that 4 of their tendons define one of the squares
of tendons.

A4.44

A4.45

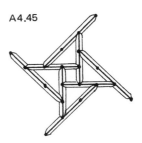

Add 4 struts, to form a distorted hexagon of tendons against
each edge of the square.

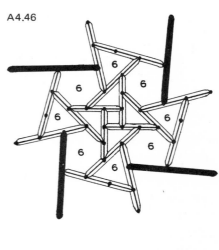

A4.46

Add 4 pairs of struts (shown in outline) to form 4 more distorted hexagons of tendons. Then add 4 more struts (shown solid), to form the first 4 undistorted hexagons of tendons.

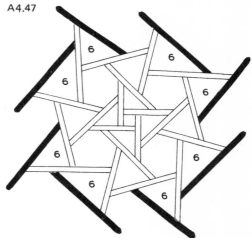

A4.47

Turn over the model. Then add 8 struts (shown solid) to form 8 more distorted hexagons of tendons.

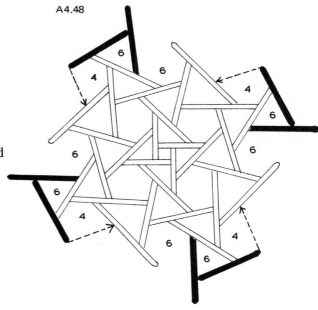

A4.48

Add 4 pairs of struts (shown solid) to form 4 more distorted hexagons of tendons. Then connect the 4 strut ends, as indicated by the arrows, to define 4 more squares of tendons.

The last 12 struts can now be added, using the cardboard model as a guide, and the figure completed. One version of this figure has struts of two different lengths; if the 24 longer ones are 9 inches long, the 24 shorter ones will be 7 1/8 inches long. The shorter struts are the ones whose ends define the 24 vertices of the squares of tendons. Each tendon should be a fraction more than one-third the length of the strut to which it forms a zigzag.

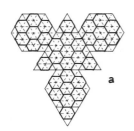

A4.49
42 struts
126 tendons

a   b

The Three-Frequency Truncated Tetrahedron (Photograph 23)

As with the two previously discussed systems, a simple cardboard
model on which the tendon network and struts are sketched will
be a very useful guide when building this Tensegrity model.
Sketch *a* shows the net diagram for a truncated tetrahedron, on
which the tendon network for this three-frequency figure is
indicated by heavy lines. Sketch *b* shows the model of the
truncated tetrahedron produced from this net diagram, with the
struts sketched on it. From such a model it can be seen that this
Tensegrity system has 42 struts and that its 126 tendons define
12 pentagons, 28 distorted hexagons, and 4 undistorted hexagons.

A4.50

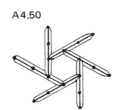

Join 6 struts so that 6 of their tendons define one of the
undistorted hexagons.

A4.51

Add 6 struts, to form a distorted hexagon of tendons against
each edge of the undistorted hexagon.

Add 6 pairs of struts, to define 6 more distorted hexagons of tendons. Then join the strut ends to the tendons, as indicated by the arrows, to define 6 of the pentagons of tendons.

A4.52

The assembly can then be turned over and the last 18 struts added, using the cardboard model as a guide, to complete the figure. One version of this figure has struts of three different lengths; if the 24 longest struts (shown solid) are 9 inches long, the 12 struts shown in outline will be 7 3/4 inches long, and the 6 struts shown shaded will be 7 5/8 inches long. Each tendon should be slightly more than one-third the length of the strut to which it forms a zigzag.

A4.53

BIBLIOGRAPHY

Fuller, R. Buckminster. *Synergetics.* New York: MacMillan, 1975.

. "Tensegrity." *Portfolio and Art News Annual* No. 4(1960):112-127, 144, 146, 148.

. *The Design Initiative.* (World Design Science Decade 1965-75, Document 2). Carbondale, Ill.: World Resources Inventory, 1963.

and Robert Marks. *The Dymaxion World of Buckminster Fuller.* New York: Doubleday, Anchor, 1973.

McHale, John. *R. Buckminster Fuller.* New York: George Braziller, 1962.

Morgan, W. *The Elements of Structure.* London: Pitman, 1964.

Pugh, Anthony J. *Polyhedra: A Visual Approach.* Berkeley: University of California Press, 1975.

U.S. Patent 3,063,521. (Tensile-integrity structures). R. B. Fuller.